TO LAIN ROADS

J.D. Goossens

Boularderie
Island Press

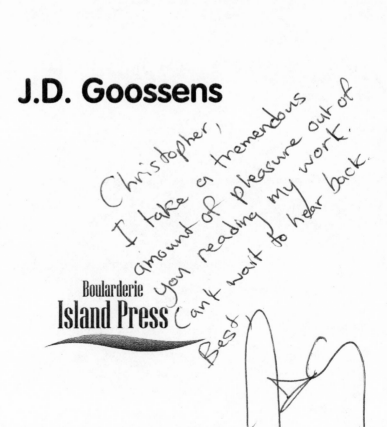

Christopher,
I take a tremendous
amount of pleasure out of
you reading my work.
Can't wait to hear back.

Best

Cover Layout by ON TIME Design harvegrant@gmail.com
Author Photo: Mike Bromley

Library and Archives Canada Cataloguing in Publication

Goossens, J. D., 1976-, author
To lain roads / J.D. Goossens.

ISBN 978-1-926448-06-0 (pbk.)

I. Title.

PS8613.O656T67 2015   C813'.6   C2015-900424-1

J.D. Goossens gooch14@hotmail.com

A Boularderie Island Press Publication

boularderieislandpress.com

PRINTED IN CANADA

For my family and hometown friends

Part One

Quick Tips for a Flawless Do-It-Yourself Painting Experience

Step 1:

There are thousands of paint types and a myriad of choices for each. Let an MPABC qualified specialist assist you in choosing the right one for the job at hand. Once selected, your paint specialist will mix the product mechanically for you at the store. Properly shaken up, the components of the paint (pigment, binder, solvent, fungicides, etc.) will be indiscernible and what will be left is a clean, unicoloured product.

DENNIS CONSTANTLY EGGED ME ON TO TELL MY LAYNE story. *He treasured its blatant 'realness' and wanted all of his friends—a veritable armada—to hear it. His network cross-sectioned the social gamut of Vancouver, British Columbia: business professionals, concert promoters, musicians, bikers, semi-pro baseball players, self-prescribing doctors, rehabilitated junkies, skateboarders, artists, interior designers. These and more, we were all drawn to him—including me, Nathan Mills, the paint salesman.*

"If you think that is rough, you need to listen to my friend Nate. You have nothing on him. Hey dude, these fine people here need a strong dose of potentialness."

"Potentialness? Definitely not a word, Den."

"Just make with your Layne Story already. Trust me guys. This is pure, unadulterated sketch," Dennis would exclaim with ringmaster buoyancy—eyes bloodshot and a bottle of homebrew (made from scratch) in his strong hand, drawing anywhere from two to sixteen eager ears to my voice and laying on me the onus to present each pair with the most engaging story they had ever heard.

Each new version of the narrative differs in some way, so it becomes difficult to keep them uniform—a pitfall of bold-faced lying.

On occasion, Dennis, the one who had heard it most, would call me out on a slip: "I thought Layne meddled with your undies," he'd blurt, questioning his own pot-muddled recollection. On the spot but quick to recover, I'd either doubt him back with questionable humour or flat-out play dumb. His implicit faith in me would win out over any and all discrepancies.

I MET DENNIS FRESH OFF MY FLIGHT FROM ST. THOMAS, Ontario—Canada's Railway Capital. My hometown is a stencil for quaintness, its systems of gullies and ravines running harmoniously with the human development. And no matter how much it wants to rain, a network of tiny dams keep the water at a steady, even flow.

Aside from its proud railway heritage, St. Thomas is perhaps best known for the bloody ploughing of an African circus elephant named Jumbo. On the night of September 15, 1885, the largest elephant in captivity and main attraction of Barnum & Bailey's Circus, Jumbo, was struck and killed by an express train in the Railway Capital. Some say Jumbo died saving a baby elephant from the braking locomotive, but accounts from the fretful night are murky with sentiment. A life-sized concrete statue of Jumbo weighing thirty-eight tons is anchored high on a hilltop at the westernmost reaches of St. Thomas to commemorate the pachyderm's historic death. But I can't help think that there are many *St. Thomasonians* who look upon the monument as a municipal hunting trophy: "Look-see what we done killed. Only the biggest pachy in captivation!"

Cattle grazed the farmlands that shelter my birthplace from the rest of the world and the rest of the world from it. These cows

ʼent years mulching grass, lowing, sleeping and getting tipped by the occasional drunk teenager, resolute to these being their only purpose in life. Until one day, when said cows were led up the chute for taps on the head and portioning. My existence prior to meeting Dennis had been an extended fluffy chapter on small town living. I, an untapped resource, decided to flee quaintness and go where the water flows in spurts and gushes or at the very least, TRY.

The WestJet plane that had departed Toronto Pearson International Airport five hours before, now started its descent toward the Vancouver skyline and the snaking Fraser River. At first take, the seemingly shoddy design of the vessel upset me. The hollow echo of the sheet metal floor, the Tupperware plastic walls, the tater-tot windows displaying telling condensation, the wobbly seats fastened in place by the merest of screws—helical threads popping like champagne corks under the slightest loss of cabin pressure a surety. I'm the plastic passenger in a child's toy, I thought in a stupid panic, 'first flight' written all over my face.

Petrified in-flight excitement sparked my nervous leg twitch, disturbing the passenger to my left. The plumpish woman wholly occupied her allotted space and was well into mine. I welcomed the intrusion, our pressed shoulders a forced intimacy that would lead to an exchange of niceties, socially-grey inflight cocktails and a hugged parting at baggage claim, but not before she left me with sage, seemingly insignificant advice that would get me out of a Vancouver pickle a year or so down the road.

Not so. She avoided eye contact and glowered at my metronomic leg. No matter, I was too amped up for concern seeing as it was my first time ever in thin air. I marveled at the rocky peaks and the creeping shadows that clouds tattooed on the landscape. With only fifty bucks to my name and a place to crash, this was easily the most whimsical maneuver of my young, safe life.

I stoked my excitement with nerdy internal commentary as we descended towards Vancouver International Airport. *This is a life-shattering move Nathan.*

Cruising out over the rippling abyss of the Pacific Ocean, I noticed we were not stopping at land's end.

What the?

Staying our westward heading, we soared farther and farther away from the coast, over a vast, unforgiving mass of black water.

Where is this pilot taking us?

The land was a shrinking crest at our backs as my leg bounced feverishly. I checked the ticket stub in the seat pouch in front of me—YVR Vancouver, as planned—and carried on the frantic struggle to identify the circumstance that was playing itself out.

This pilot is on a suicide run.

The terror made me sure of it, as I worked out the minute details of why this psycho determined to plunge the only plane I have ever boarded into the hard Pacific sheath below, a soon to be watery grave for everyone on board. I glanced down at the expanse of current to approximate time of impact. The ocean kicked up tiny white waves, as though licking its million lips.

The guy caught his wife in bed with one of the stewards. Yep, that's it.

The terror made me sure of it. Even gave the pilot a name: Gareth, and his hussy of a wife Mona.

He is going to ground the plane into the ocean. He is going to ocean the plane!

This flight was meant to symbolize the end of my past life, not actualize it.

Did I live a good life? Was I good?

Will Gareth announce his intentions over the intercom and apologize for them?

The pilot dipped the right wing, the side I was on, and my gut sank. I slowly bent over pretending to knot my shoelace, groping for the location of the sub-seat life preserver on my way back upright.

A toddler in the seat directly ahead of mine turned his head to marvel at the expanse of sea beneath him. Unaware of any impending danger, the tike envisioned the animated creatures from his Disney films playing their games below the surface. Best that he didn't know the truth. I paused to envy his ignorance. The thought seized as the plane snapped down. Water leaked into the right-side windows, sky in the left. Gareth had decided to follow through with 'Operation: Spite Tramp'. This was it.

At the very least, wait for the oxygen masks and an alarm of some kind before you shrill in terror. Go out with a morsel of dignity.

Demeanors unchanged, the other passengers went about their in-flight business of drumming laptops, picking pretzels out of their teeth and reading.

Are you all brain-dead? Does nobody see?

Suddenly, a relinquishing calm swept over me, and I melodramatically consoled myself.

I had the chance to see the majesty of these mountains before I died. And my family and friends will grieve horribly, so that's something.

The plane leveled out its forty-five degree slant, dropped landing gear and headed back towards the shore for touchdown. Turns out, some of the landing strips are positioned such that pilots need to swoop out over the water to angle in on them, and far enough to leave room for a Boeing 737-800 to make a U turn.

You're a tool.

My first ever landing freaked me out fiercely. The jolt and heavy whir of airflow as the vessel struggled to slow its landing speed felt like it would implode at any second. My nerves were shot. I sat exhausted, completely still as my muscles relaxed. I dabbed residual salty fret from my forehead and under my nose, and merciful Gareth nosed us towards a big glass wall. As I composed myself, I detected a snide grin on the face of the lady beside me. She had sensed the current of pitiable panic working me over the past four minutes.

A housefly meandered past our row. I considered the precariousness of its travel. And in the air of change, I interpreted my far-from-death experience as a preamble to adventure; a sign that good or bad, land or crash, Vancouver would be an exhilarating place to live. Not even uncertain death could stand in the way.

THE INTOXICATION OF ADVENTURE GAVE ME
the sensation that each moment in my life held a measure
of uniqueness from the rest, a feeling you crave after years of
swimming in a small pond bumping into the same fish, the same
muddy walls. We farmed fish become attuned to change, though
we're not necessarily equipped for it. Everything was novel and
big. My need for shelter was met by my older cousin Angie who
had lived in Vancouver her entire life. Offered a reconfigured
closet generally used as a computer station, I found her generosity
humbling.

She rented the main floor of a house on West 41st down from
Kerrisdale's main drag, which included highbrow businesses
like upmarket furniture emporiums, handbag repositories,
jewelry shops and fashion boutiques. A well-to-do community on
Vancouver's west-end, Kerrisdale sat south of its younger hipper
brother Kitsilano; two areas in Vancouver proper where the birds
eloquently tweet and chirp but never squawk, and where city
officials race to keep garbage off of the streets.

My very first night in Vancouver Angie asked if I would join her
on a jog through the neighbourhood. To her, it was the perfect

opportunity to get reacquainted and a play for safety considering the time of night. To me physically, it seemed borderline impossible.

"It's a big moon tonight, but crazies lurk everywhere in this city, not only East Hastings," she advised.

Knowing I'd be hungry from the flight Angie plucked me a banana from the bunch in her kitchen. She also provided me with her rollerblades—big on me, fluorescent pink—assuming I couldn't keep up on foot. A fair call considering her cardiovascular regimen of sixty-minute runs six days a week and mine of zero running seven days a week. Not to mention she had six inches on me and legs to my navel. With the banana in my hand, we would have looked like a giraffe/penguin relay team.

To her word, she kept brisk pace on the sidewalks of those pristine backstreets. I bladed the roadway beside her, challenged to keep up, body parts flailing like a cartoon villain on a splay of marbles.

Living on nearly opposite ends of the country all our lives, we had plenty to share. Angie did most of the talking. I heard of her struggles with academics: enrolment in a Master's program in Art History and uncertain about her desire to proceed. And her love life: dated Jeffrey two months and uncertain of her desire to proceed.

"Good with the three-month decisions, bad with the three-year decisions, story of my life. Why is there always someone or something wanting to lock me up? And where does this need for escape come from?"

Angie didn't desire answers from me the newly landed hillbilly. She just needed a neutral sounding board. I picked up on this from the file of questions she had already spoken through.

"I'm sorry Nate. You only just arrive and I'm already subjecting you to my dramas."

"I'm, I'm fine. Good, good stuff." Out of breath, I couldn't counterbalance the conversation anyhow.

Many of the houses on our trek were set back from the road, with vast lawns that require entire afternoons to cut. I imagined the timed sprinkler heads rising out of the ground like submarine periscopes. Each blade of grass seemed to be set in place with tweezers, prim turf foreground to massive structures—eight or nine bedrooms for some, I guessed. The facades were cold glaring faces. Black bedroom eyes, pointy porch-top noses and long slithery concrete tongues unraveling serpent-like from door mouths. A number of the homes were built with stately pillars at their fronts; white fangs guarding the wealthy. Sickly grandiose, I thought.

Thirty-five minutes in, Angie gave no indication of tiring out. It may have been my exhaustion playing tricks, but she picked-up speed with every climb. Dizzily low on kilojoules, I craved sustenance but my throat was too parched to even consider snacking on my banana. Undernourished and mired in dilemma, my brain defocused to the sound of sand and stone crumpling between my wheels and the asphalt, resonating to the ossicles of my inner-ear.

Running us alongside a high stone wall, Angie asked out of the blue: "You cool with cemeteries?"

"Sure," I said breathlessly. Thinking, in my oxygen-deprived mind, that the dead have to be stowed away somewhere, right? Before I realized her intentions the rock wall gave way to a yawning wrought-iron gateway and we were entering one.

"Shortcut," she put challengingly, spinning on her feet to catch my expression.

"Perfect." My smile marginally hid my trepidation.

I was soon at ease. Pristinely laid out, it was more like a country club for the deceased. The grass was trimmer than an Aussie cricket pitch and the monuments brought modesty to its knees. Life-size statuettes, metal busts, intricate carvings, tall spires, wall shrines and mausoleums made of opulent stone. The largest and most immoderate of pedestals stood at the intersecting laneways and reached some fifteen feet high. Lavishness idealized the dead rich, aiming to elevate them above the thrall of society even in the face of the ultimate equalizer. Corner lots in life, corner plots in death.

Bury me in the g.d. woods for all I give a d., I thought, peeved. In the words of my mother, and her mother before her, *I could have spit*. But I couldn't have spit, because my mouth was desiccated. Instead I brightened, imagining how the weather would erode the noses on the busts.

I DISCOVERED THAT FRIENDS IN VANCOUVER WERE AT a premium. A sad nil, really. Angie's addiction to education left her little to no time for a social life. On her second Master's degree, she had built a formidable foundation of knowledge, though I had the feeling that her current major—Medieval Art History—would be the dusty storage attic to her intellectual property.

Rumour had it that a full-time job sops up forty hours of friendlessness per week, pays the rent, and keeps you in food, so I got one. Angie's dad, my Uncle Jerry, arranged a job interview on my behalf. A born salesman, Uncle Jerry was a big wheel in Vancouver, the one I rode into a potential career.

I had spoken briefly with a manager from the company by telephone:

"That uncle of yours is a wild man. Got a post-secondary education son?"

"Yes sir. A Commerce deg..."

"I don't even think Jerry graduated high school. Boy, that nutter can talk. A friggin' wild man!"

"He sure..."

"I could tell you a story or two. Come see me Monday and tell that uncle of yours to shove it!"

Based on such a conversation, I was invited to be interviewed for a position at Briscoll Inc. The nature of the opening was left unclear to me in the hype surrounding Uncle Jerry.

Utterly unprepared, I was fearful leading up to the interview. I had let pass a golden opportunity to acquire valuable job hunting skills during my final year at McMaster University. Over the course of my last semester recruiters would visit the school to court future business graduates. The process, aptly named 'On-Campus Recruiting', was a hectic series of job postings, corporate presentations, interview sessions, resume workshops and interview effectiveness training. On-Campus Recruiting rose to pandemic status within the graduating class. The students went mad dying to become the next go-getter assimilated into a large firm. Concerned about their headway in comparison with fellow student candidates, their gossip bucketed from the classrooms and hallways.

"Did you hear that Arthur Anderson is coming to OCR?" The truly annoying students used the acronym. "I heard they drive you off campus in a limo for your third interview."

"Heard the latest? Tony from marketing flopped his fourth-rounder, one away from a sixty-thou base."

"Tina signed for forty thou with Enterprise, but her bonus structure is crap compared to Ron's."

On it went with benefit packages, company cars, gas allowances, moving expenses. After the first month, urges to torch the OCR headquarters started contaminating my daily thoughts. I wasn't harping on the goals and ambitions of my colleagues. By all means achieve, achieve to your wallet's content. Just do it without the nonsense.

The pressures ballooned to ridiculousness near year end. To my surprise, the graduating class escaped without a reported murder, suicide or murder-suicide. But the whole charade poisoned my being. So I boycotted. No workshops, resumes or interviews.

Admittedly, the ban built momentum once I'd realized the time it freed up in my schedule. But buried beneath my morning sleep-ins, mid-morning viewings of The Price Is Right, afternoon viewings of The Days of Our Lives, and weeknight drinking binges, there was an around-the-clock Just Cause. I didn't bother trying to recruit anyone to the protest. Didn't picket, didn't call in a bomb threat or take a billy stick blow from riot police. Historically it was the feeblest protest ever assembled. There was only me—refusing to participate, refusing to assimilate, or even get off the couch.

I stared into the bathroom mirror on that chilled Vancouver morning, the day of my first official job interview. A brown suit two sizes too small and a dated tie two shades too grey, my overgrown hair spilling out over my ears and ruffling at the back, looking like the crossbreed of Pee-Wee Herman and the Incredible Hulk mid-rage (without the muscle), I regretted for the first time my OCR ban in university.

You look stupid. Why couldn't you be normal? Join the ranks of the rest of your classmates? Learn the skills your parents paid tens of thousands of dollars to have you learn? Twenty-three and never interviewed? You are a righteous idiot. Didn't want to be another sheep, eh? Well, look at you now Mr. L. Wolf.

I smeared Angie's mousse in my hair to try and hide some of the shag up under the rest. It looked wavy and terrible and was quickly drying to an unsalvageable state.

Despite my nervous fidgeting in the back seat, the aged cabbie of eastern European descent kept stone quiet as he made our way to the southernmost edge of Vancouver proper, an industrial pocket of box-shaped manufacturing and warehousing facilities —lumber yards, printing factories, auto wreckers—built for functionality rather than aesthetics. Though the Fraser River ran along its bank, it was still a grubby, uninspiring place. The waterway, an ambling thoroughfare for tugboats towing lumber, showed few signs of life: murky and brown, heartbroken over having to course through the ugliness. If Vancouver was an antiquated steamer and the downtown its ballroom, this was its coal furnace.

The cabbie turned down a side street near the shoreline of the river and slowed at a long two-level building shaped like a retirement cake. Surrounded by wire fencing and painted a fainting Baby Chick (344-28) with Shy Cherry (936-41) trim, its colour and rectangularity stole me back to my hometown's hockey arena, a place Dad zealously took me at daybreak on Saturdays to suck at hockey.

The main gate led to a small parking lot. My cab driver bottomed-out his ride on the steep laneway. Scrape! I cringed with mortification, imagining a host of cartoon eyes glaring out of dark slits in the window blinds.

The parking stalls were full to capacity. Four spaces against the building held luxury vehicles with the sun gleaming on their detailed exteriors. The remaining eight spaces along the fence at the property line were occupied by rusty, entry-level cars. Trees from the property next door overhung the fence and as a result the hoods were stained with leaching tree buds and copious amounts of bird turd. The company name and logo were embossed on a front door made of thick glass and polished metal.

This had to work. *It had to.*

I was greeted by a young blonde woman sitting at a reception desk. She was thinly built with aquamarine eyes and full puckered lips painted Coral Gables (073-12). Her skin was softly bronzed by the summer sun. A desert rose in this greasy wasteland.

Beautiful women are intimidators in my world. They are Marvel Comic villains who release a toxin that incapacitates me. I barely mumbled my name and the purpose of my visit, offering her limited eye contact. She was hideously gorgeous; a real menace. My throat dried to a rich paste and my right knee felt like it was about to buckle and give away my leg. She brushed her hair in back of her ear and lifted a phone to it—the oblong receiver accentuated against the sweeping contours of her stunning face. I didn't dare gawp at her long.

"Bert, Nathan Mills is here to see you…. Alright then."

She put the phone down and smiled blandly. "Please take a seat. Bert will be with you shortly," she said, pointing to the four plush chairs along the wall opposite her desk. The chairs were bordered by a water cooler and a magazine table.

"Thanks you," I said in a pubertal crackle. Familiar with this reaction, she grinned a grin that said: Pull yourself together and sit. I quickly found a seat and hid behind a copy of Macleans magazine with a picture of Hitler on the cover.

The reception area impressed with a high ceiling and skylight. Two modern light fixtures hung down from long cords, illuminating flawless paintwork done in Oxford Stone (665-42) and an intricate flooring system. The concrete subfloor had been overlaid in polished brown pebbles the size of chickpeas and held tightly down by a clear glossy glue. The shimmer from the overhead lights and the continuation of the floor into an open hallway made it look as though a river of rock flowed throughout the space.

Photographs and plaques marked the wall to my right. The two framed pictures were of the same moustached man fraternizing with political leaders. In one, the man posed with then Prime Minister Jean Chretien. In the other he was locked in the heartiest of handshakes with, according to the caption, China's Ambassador of Trade Xi Cho Chin. Both of them were joyfully red-faced, drunk on commerce. Encircling the photos were various awards for achievement in business.

This is serious business, I thought, petrified for my life. The big time.

At long last he arrived (he later divulged his strategy of making people wait, whether busy or not, to give the impression of a healthy demand on his time). Bert was medium height and thinly built, with fluffy cocoa hair and a matching moustache. I put him in his forties and deemed him ferret-like.

Well-groomed, Bert was not the intoxicated man in the photographs. He had tidily donned a bright white golf shirt with the company logo, beige pants, and mahogany leather loafers. Together we had a lot of brown happening.

"Bert Francis." He walked towards me with his hand outstretched prematurely. I rose up to meet him part way to get to that discomfitting, dangling hand and shake it.

"Nathan Mills, or Nate," I said. Sounding unsure of my own

name and noting Bert's fanatical squeeze.

"Thank you Chantelle." Bert winked at the immobilizing force behind the desk, adding a playful smile. I glanced over my shoulder for her reaction.

"Never a problem Bert," she offered back half-heartedly, eyes rolling away.

Bert led me down the stream of rock into the hallway. He let out an exaggerated exhale, squinted his eyes and pointed into his chest with a hitchhiker thumb. Either he was pointing through himself to Chantelle as if to say 'She is so smoking hot' or pointing at himself to say 'She wants me bad.' Either one made for a highly unprofessional gesture and the latter had a delusionary smack.

As we walked the hallway of closed doors leading to his office, he shared an anecdote about drinking with my Uncle Jerry before interrupting himself to point out an aerial photograph hanging in the hallway. "The Vanderpost Estates. We have the contract to recoat their seven buildings and seal the cobblestone courtyard every five years. Guess who closed the deal? Your very own Uncle Jerry, back when he worked here. We call it 'The Jerry Special'."

"Wow," I said dutifully.

Bert's orderly office matched the man and we sat on opposite ends of a composite wood desk, the large window to our side framing the segregated parking lot. Bert coolly introduced me to Briscoll Inc. The company manufactured industrial products for use on new construction and restorative projects. Their focus was concrete, and they had designed products to meet any concrete need: sealing, coating, repairing, strengthening, loosening, cleaning, patching, waterproofing, colouring, etc. They boasted market share in fifty countries worldwide. Bert concerned himself with only one of them, as his official title was Domestic Sales Manager.

Bert's first interview question was not 'Would you be willing to grow us a moustache?' Instead he plied me with a much broader stroke: "What do you bring to the table?"

Although my answers were groggily clichéd, they were delivered with none of the sheepishness for which I am known.

My voice had volume and did not crackle once. But the early momentum quickly waned when challenged by a doozy of a second question: "What would you say is your biggest weakness?"

I'm a perfectionist. No.

I'm a workaholic. No.

These were the stock answers I denied myself. I needed an original response this time to avoid sounding like a textbook reading, but nothing came to me. The socially allotted time for response was quickly passing and so desperately I blurted: "I'm an avid daydreamer."

"I'm sorry Nate, you daydream?" Bert verified.

"Yes. I often have these vivid images of places I'd rather be. They can be distracting."

It had sounded better inside my head, had me coming off as imaginative and clever, as a welcome splash of colour, of visionariness, different from his other robotic candidates. Instead I presented myself as an inattentive flake. Like those little league baseball kids that pick dandelions or stare at cloud formations as the game goes on around them.

"What places?" Bert asked, wearing the thinnest smile.

Stranded outside of the box, I felt my face flush red and the voice crackle return. "Other countries, like Australia," I managed.

"Are you with me right now?"

"I really am," I assured him with shortened breath, aware of the rising heat to my neck.

We both chuckled apprehensively.

Why not tell him about your uncontrollable urge to set things on fire, huh Nathan.

Bert exploited the awkward hiccup in our proceedings to suggest a guided tour of the complex. At the end of the corridor a coffee maker was burbling a line of java into a glass pot. After scoring a cup for himself Bert suggested we view Production in action.

The door beyond was plastered with warnings in the prudent colours yellow and red: precautionary messages paired with cartoon illustrations concerning health, safety and building security. There were four in total.

Visitors must sign-in at reception! (cartoon human with briefcase)
Warning: Heavy forklift traffic inside. Be alert! (cartoon eyes)
Eye protection is mandatory! (cartoon human wearing sunglasses)
Protective footwear required! (cartoon human with spike lodged in foot)

"Pop in for a quick look," said Bert, reaching into a cloth pouch nailed to the door and pulling out two pairs of yellow-tinted safety glasses. "Lotta good these'll do if a rack of fifty-pound pails falls on our coconuts. Am I right? Trust me, with Bill the Spill back here, we need all the protection we can get."

We put on the glasses and the world shone a happy yellow. A nerdier looking Bert regaled me with inventory volumes and average monthly sales data, but I was concentrating on the bright yellow tinge of everything, daydreaming of a procedure that could permanently set my vision to this golden frequency.

"These monkeys are maniacs on their forklifts, so keep an eye out," Bert cautioned as he opened the door. My yellow fantasy dispersed.

Forklifts zipped to and fro, dropping off metal drums of raw material and picking up pallets of finished product. Overbearing the forklift motors were the roars of heavier machinery to the back of the facility, some nerve centre beyond our vantage point.

The plant had the floor plan of a grocery store, two wide rows connected by aisles. The door we passed through opened onto **Aisle 1: Storage**. Metal scaffolding with plywood flats formed three levels of load-bearing shelving where buckets of finished product were housed. Towering forty feet high, this fortification of manufactured goods cast an imposing shadow over me.

"Let's move." Bert pointed at the row to our right and walked us in the direction of the louder noise.

The stone floor had given way to rigid floor paint in a dulled shade of Utah Sky (959-32). Later during my indoctrination I learned it to be Dura Wear, the industrial epoxy floor coating system. Dura Wear was designed with space age technology and is suitable for any industrial space requiring a tough-as-nails floor that defends against scratching, chipping, fading, foot-traffic, and chemical attack. Dura Wear even wards off the spread of bacteria, as the workers on the poultry kill floors at B.C. Foods will validate. Dura Wear cleans up with ease and can be tinted to a select variety of pastel colours. At a price of $1.12 per square foot, there is no other system that can provide better value for your company dollar.

We reached **Aisle 2: Coatings and Sealants** and made contact with plant manager Ron Thompson. At six-five, two-twenty, he was a daunting stack of man. "Come back here to learn what real work is about, huh Bertrand?" Ron talked down to Bert with finely calibrated contempt. He was a tank of muscle; a physical marvel for a man of fifty-five years with salt-and-pepper hair and hardened good looks.

"Actually I'm showing Nate here the fruits of my labour." Bert struck back meagrely, never looking more the ferret than in Ron's gorillian shadow.

"Right, is that what you call your two-hour lunches at the Fraser Arms?"

"Anyways, Ron."

"Anyways, Bertrand."

The story goes that one lunch hour, on his way back from a supply run, Ron was certain he saw Bert's Toyota Camry in the parking lot of the local gentleman's club. (Coincidentally Bert later treated me to lunch there to celebrate my one-year anniversary with the firm. The doorman knew his name).

"Nate might be our new inside guy. Nate, Ron. Ron runs Production."

"Yep," Ron said half-heartedly, staring right through me. Clearly I was just another pencil-pusher to him. I offered my hand and it disappeared into his cavernous mitt.

"Nate is Jerry's nephew," Bert added.

Ron's grip tightened. I imagined him tearing my arm clean from my body.

"Jerry? You don't say. It's a real pleasure, but please excuse me," Ron looked at Bert and puffed up his chest. "Some of us *actually* work around here." He motioned towards Aisle 1, then turned round for a few parting words: "Bertrand, hire this kid. He comes from good stock. And don't let me catch you back here without steel-toes on your feet again."

Bert waited until Ron was out of earshot to gripe (not far, considering the racket of the place). "Stupid ape! Nate, these plant guys don't realize who butters the bread around here." He pointed down **Aisle 2: Coatings and Sealants** to the seven workmen in matching coveralls toiling around three identical metal contraptions that looked like giant cake blenders. Three of the men were sapping a gelatinous substance (Cinnamon Toast 983-98), from one of the tanks with a stack of empty pails and a weigh scale.

"Too many monkeys, not enough bananas," Bert mocked the lot.

I laughed to win favour, exhaling dignity with each hoot; my first corporate butt-lick.

We moved on to **Aisle 3: Powders**. The powder products were generated in two large U-shaped vats made of flexile suede by two men decked out in gas masks and protective coveralls—the rubber Hazmat kind that disease researchers wear to stave off the irony of catching what they're curing. In the talcum brume I could see the costumed workers outlined on a metal catwalk that joined the gaping sacks. Machinery exuded a harrowing scream. This, combined with the chalky air, left me temporarily incapacitated.

"Here we make our cementitious grouts, fillers and admixtures. Look at those two clowns. Make a good ad for a university. Am I right?"

My sympathy for the two shadows in the powdery haze was obstructed by thoughts of cement dust being sucked into my healthy pink lungs, mixing with the moisture present, and hardening into a concrete butterfly under my chest. I shortened my breaths.

"This room can age you ten years in a day. Stay in here any longer and we'll start to look like these two jerks. You get the idea anyway."

(In time, I met the men of **Aisle 3: Powders**, Kevin and Karl. They were simple, good-natured guys, and looked fifteen years older than their ages.)

Bert gestured for me to follow him back to his office. He checked his wristwatch after dropping his safety specs back into the cloth bag. For the past hour Bert had strutted around the place like a nightclub owner, acting hard and degrading men who he perceived as lower in stature, as if to overcompensate for his skinny arm requiring extra punch-holes in his wrist strap.

"Christ, it's ten o'clock. Position starts at twenty-five thousand with a comprehensive benefits package. You can come in on Monday. Does that work for you?" Bert announced.

"Uh, yes?"

"Good. See you Monday at seven. And tell that uncle of yours that Bert F. says to turn down the bullshit."

BIG STUFF HAPPENED IN 2000 IN SPITE OF ME. IT WAS declared World Mathematical Year for starters. The last natural pyrenean ibex was found dead, apparently killed by a falling tree. Tuanku Syed Sirajuddin became the Raja of Perlis. The constitution of Finland was rewritten. Sony launched PlayStation 2. Oh, and George W. Bush defeated Al Gore for the presidency of the United States after a lengthy Floridian recount.

Monday came with asphyxiating cloud cover and heavy rain, and launched my tenure with Briscoll Inc.

"See this? This is my most important tool. When I reach for this, it means I'm about to unload some product on a guy," Bert said first thing Monday morning. He was holding a stapler in front of my face in my tiny new office. "You staple your receipts to the pink invoices. Now plant your name on that sucker." Bert regally presented me with a small hand-held label maker like it was the Order of Canada medallion and stood over my chair as I punched out my name. He watched me with as much intent as my father did at my First Communion, which made me fumble the machine nervously. It wasn't until I had stuck the blue label to the stapler that I'd realized it read 'NATHAM'.

"Oh." The two of us stared at the blunder a long couple seconds, giving the mistake its due. Fluorescent tubes lighting the office hummed us a steady backbeat.

I'd started into a replacement label when Bert relieved me of the device. "We can live with that one. Just a label, am I right Natham?"

Chantelle called Bert over the office PA system to field a call from a customer. I sat alone with NATHAM for twenty-five minutes, wasting staples. Bert returned to find me swiveling around on my chair in an attempt to beat my old record of four full rotations. "R & D, let's move," he said with a look that added *Sorry to interrupt your game.*

A nearby door opened to a zigzag of stairs which led to more office space. Out another jam we traversed down narrow labyrinthian hallways to a large observation window. The pane was the size of French doors and bordered by stained wood trim (Hazeltine 901-23). On the opposite side of the spotless glass was a spotless white laboratory. A male and female technician stood facing us at an island counter wearing clear safety glasses over prescription eyewear, white surgical masks, white neoprene gloves and white lab coats. Each had been brushing goo (Hummingbird Jasper 540-03) onto individual concrete tiles. These were actual scientists, comparing coagulation and curing times. Quantifying and hypothesizing. Observing and manipulating nature with its own laws. I was humbly impressed.

"I started people on calling it the nerdbowl," Bert bragged. Not one to wait for audience approval, he laughed proudly, sounding like a scavenging hyena. "Joking aside, we dedicate a substantial amount of time and energy to quality assurance and new product development. Part and parcel to the sales pitch." Bert had held his lab fish in slightly higher standing than his warehouse simians.

Cordial introductions to the staff, touring the rest of the facilities and viewing a sixty-minute promotional video on the corporation had swept me into lunchtime somewhat underwhelmed. *This is going to be a cinch*, I thought to myself as I observed my new coworkers interacting in the break room. Really, the hardest task that day had been slyly lusting over Receptionist Chantelle enjoying her chunky salad. Her eyes shut and mouth oh so wide around quartered vegetables lubed in extra virgin olive oil. *To be the next lazy cut of cucumber in line for her fork,* I thought in secret.

After lunch, Bert sat me in a small glassed-in meeting room with a round table, four chairs (none swivel) and a fern in one corner. I was to review Briscoll's product information binder and fill out hiree paperwork for the next two hours while Bert caught up on his morning load. Like I'd surmised, this job was going to be a cakewalk.

The two hours leapt by. I was drunk on product specifications and feeling mid-afternoon drowsy when Bert decided the best way to train me was to throw me into the fire. "Learn or burn," was his hardy advice. So I spent my last three hours of the day sweating it out on the phone lines with a stack of Briscoll reference binders on my desk. Contractors older than my father, some with up to forty years of experience in the industry, called for advice on any number of the forty-seven products we manufactured.

"This is Nathan. How can I help you?"

"Can I get a technical rep, I need ideas."

"I, I am…this is. You got one."

"You sound pretty young. Then again, I'm too old to be doing this shit. Listen here Nate: I have an overhead, below-grade crack in a multi-level car park. The leak is active and the concrete is leaching rust from the rebar and a white efflorescence from the slab. There is a second problem area at a cold joint."

"OK," I responded, engulfed in confusion and scrambling to write down meaningless words.

"Positive-end repair is not an option thanks to some asshole laying Peel-and-Stick in the planter."

"Idiots."

"I'll say. So am I looking at urethane injection? If so, what size ports for a quarter-inch? At what angle? How much liquid for ten feet? I have a kanga gun with a diamond blade if need be but I don't want to use any crumbly quick set crap, or crystallizing grouts, or any polymer overlays."

"I see, I see." The cry of a Help Desk operator burning alive.

"Well?"

"Can I get your name and number and call you back? I want

to confirm this with a fellow rep," I said; this line became my canned answer for utter technical confusion.

"Put the other guy on if he knows more than you. Time is money."

"He's not available at the moment."

"Hurry it up! And get *him* to call me back! Fuck." The f-bomb I overheard as he was hanging up the line. It rattled me no less.

I worked late that night and took literature home to read, falling asleep on Angie's couch, beside an open binder, in my work clothes and shoes. I would be found working late most nights. Bert carted me to tradeshows with him every other Saturday. Fortunately I had no money or social life to impede my progress. My salary after taxes and hours logged, was in the ballpark of about twelve-bucks an hour.

I call it my non-year because in my world, nothing happened. Here is my 2000 year-in-review:

Angie moved in with Jeffrey, I took over the rent.

Work, work, work.

Found episodes of the game show Bumper Stumpers archived on the net—RUNVS.

Work, work, work.

One morning, cracked an egg with a double yolk—great dipping.

Work, work, work.

Received four GST rebate checks from the government.

Work, work, work.

Counted the coins in my change jar.

I worked the job, the job worked me. Toenails cut, shoes polished, meals cooked, dishes cleaned, garbage disposed, butt wiped—ticks on a to-do list. The mundanity that gets lost in the back country of our longterm memory becoming unused footage in the movie of one's life. I touched no-one but myself that year and by summer's end, had the feeling I was tuning an instrument I would never play.

A life unfit for even the cutting room floor.

"IF IT SUCKS SO HARD, WHY HAVEN'T WE QUIT?" I YELLED over the blast of one of Dennis's thrash metal cassette tapes.

"Don't worry about me. My days are so fucking numbered." This was Dennis's motto for his disenchanting work life at Briscoll Inc. In boring monthly meetings, Dennis had become the one mouthing his credo across the boardroom and watching me crack up, or proclaiming it on trips from the plant in his 1975 GMC Sierra Classic short-box. Poverty prevented the purchase of anything less rusty (or olive-green) and the truck's bed was always full of tree buds and bird turd, but it was a welcomed reprieve from public transit.

I had met Dennis, International Sales, in the print room on my second day at work. He was photocopying hockey pools. "Yo new guy, six pack for your silence." He'd said, shuffling his paperwork. I'd won a ride home with him that night and from there on in we were buds. It seems a crude leap from chance meeting to sharing innermost hopes and fears, but we made the jump.

Dennis Zimmer possessed none of the traits that garnered popularity back in my hamlet of St. Thomas. Take athleticism. Forget even basic coordination, Dennis lacked the most rudimentary of sporting fundamentals. He dribbled a basketball to his eyes and shot it from his waist granny-style. He skated on his ankles, wristed the bowling ball, lifted his head on his golf shots, dipped his elbow at the plate. He kicked like my great aunt, threw like my mom, caught like my sister and ran like a wounded African antelope. In the lingo of my hometown friends: a Sally Struthers of the sports world.

Next up to the plate—looks. It happens that two physically ugly people can produce an attractive child. Though rare, features hiding in the crevasses of asymmetry can be passed down evenly to the offspring and beauty is served; two wrongs reproducing a right. Not so in Dennis's case, where ugly was born unto ugly (that I myself am far from fair permits me to speak freely). Like shy teenagers at a prom, his parents' physical features intermingled awkwardly. His woe-is-me aspect included a network of tree bark wrinkles stalking from the corner of his eyes to his floppy earlobes, folds the size of which no crow could track behind— terradactyl's feet, possibly. Bright red capillaries like shattered panes of stained glass ran their circuitry on his translucent face. The same side-saddle part his mother had combed after baths divided his hair, just as the fly-away crown that she'd tamed with her spittle still had a mind of its own. A gangly white frame hinged by an incongruous beer belly fronted an outbreak of turd-like moles on his shoulder blades that protruded vulnerably, as if his skin was blowing fart bubbles. Tight hide around his thin neck displayed the working parts: thick blue veins and a mercurial ping pong ball of an Adam's apple bounding between pronounced pillars. Varicose veined, thin fingered, wide-footed, droopy breasted, hairy backed, mono-browed, crook-nosed, buttless, his entire body was a trouble area.

Dennis was neither rich nor musical nor fashionable nor macho nor a brawler, nor did he know the lyrics to the latest Celine Dion releases (kidding). Nor did he drive a fast car or brag about bedding choice women. The draw was how Dennis made you feel: on point; on board; onto something. I had been unfamiliar with a person's worth being gauged along those lines. I preferred this new yardstick; I hadn't registered a single notch on the old one.

Dennis once told me that he fixated his efforts on two personality traits. The first: honesty with others, but more importantly, with yourself. The second: accountability for your actions. He once said: "I don't care who you are or what you have going for yourself, if you are wise, or about to pack a bowl, we should talk." Those who embodied his core values he dubbed 'wise'. Dennis also loved his weed. "I love weed," he'd often say in a strained moan, a freshly-inhaled toke held tight to his lungs like a warm hug. A THC high Dennis described as the 'synchronization of the senses'; 'liberation from the bondage of linear thought'; 'journeyman's doorway to an uncharted metaphysical dimension' (I instantly corrected his application of the word 'journeyman'). 'Floaty Town', I associated with seizures of voiceless paranoia and cases of the stupids. But Dennis was a great person. He acted without an underlying agenda. We'd talk about life from time to time, and afterward I'd come out feeling alive and important. We made for good friends, Dennis and I. Or so I thought before my Layne Story.

This had been a particularly bad day at the office (most were), and Dennis went off. "You hear the way that Arthur prick speaks to me?" he yelled over the music and his struggling engine. "The stooge thinks I'm his kid or something? Fucking place. That's it dude, I've said it before but this time, I'm tellin' ya, they're sooooo fucking numbered!"

"Course they are Den."

"Enough. No more Briscoll talk. Gets Betsy agitated. Doesn't it girl." Dennis had named his truck Betsy, but used her pet name, Piglet, more often. "Who cares dude? It's Friday and we've got your first Cleansing tomorrow!" Dennis had left me in the dark as to what a Cleansing entailed, wanting it to be a surprise. It sounded like a baptism of some sort. Whatever it was, he was passionate about it.

"What do you wear to your first Cleansing? A white cloak?" I asked him.

"Super casual," he replied, offering up nothing more.

I met Dennis at a downtown apartment building at Thurlow and Robson at eleven a.m. the next day. I was equal parts excited and edgy, scratching at my bushy hair and eyebrows and chewing my nails all morning long. An invite to a party like this would never happen in St. Thomas, and maybe that was a good thing. He was all parts excited and hugged me tight on the street before leading us to the entrance. Dennis was a hugger. Not one man in St. Thomas had been a hugger. Actually, there had been one. He'd ended up leaving town in order to live a certain way.

Dennis pressed the button for the Sibley unit.

"I'm already baptized Roman Catholic *and* circumcised. So?" I joked nervously as we waited. He just grinned and kept his eyes trained on the buzzer system.

The locking mechanism on the door let out an overly loud hum and we went inside. Bypassing a wide stairwell Dennis led us down a hallway with a stink that would floor a farmhand. It smelled warm, medicinal and conjured. And though I've never been to a tannery, that's how I imagined it would smell.

We stopped at the last door at the end of the hallway. The source of the stench.

"Nothing gets you cleaner than a dozen Hail Mary's. So?" I said, trying to put on nonchalance. A wordless Dennis led us through the unlocked door and the apartment's entranceway.

He made no mention of the heavy odour, nor the large man passed out upright on the sofa, his face a pale green, mouth wide open, and a weird brown bottle propped between his legs. The large flask had a finger hook near the spout and I first thought it looked like a medieval potion bottle.

Three strides later the kitchen came into view to our right. Two men wearing white aprons soiled with amber smears were tending to a massive kettle that boiled on two stovetop burners. A third aproned man was draining a reddish liquid out of a tall plastic bucket through a jerry-rigged spout at the base. All stopped their courses of action to acknowledge our arrival, but said nothing. A fourth man emerged from the kitchen wearing a button-up shirt and khakis and holding another of the brown bottles.

"Dennis!" he said, giving him a warm embrace. Another hugger.

Then he turned to me and raised the bottle. "Hefeweizen. We need you to drink this up."

I scrunched my face and glanced over at Dennis for some insight. He gave back an apologetic, 'oh well' shrug. An expression I had yet to see him don in our short friendship.

At that exact moment, I realized I hardly knew Dennis at all and that his social life was mostly a mystery to me. A video they played us in high school at a Catholic retreat, about the dangers of cults, came quickly to mind. It dramatized how they prey on the lonely and disenfranchised (me) and how their leaders lure people in with their charm and charisma (Dennis). I started to question the details of my situation, and my adrenaline fired, feeling like a billion tiny soldiers charging up my throat. *What happened to that sickly guy on the couch? Rod didn't even think to comment on him? What is Hefeweizen? The name of their deity? Cultspeak for newbie? Latin for slave? Norse for concubine? Why do 'we' need me to drink poison? Whose 'we'? What the hell are they boiling down in that kitchen? Why does it stink to high Heaven? What's that Them's the brakes look on Dennis's stupid mug? Did I just hear a deadbolt slide into place?*

"Don't worry, Nate, right? This is not your average homebrew. We need the bottle for our next batch, so drive that into you."

Hefeweizen is the name of a delicious German wheat beer, beer sometimes bottled in traditional carafes known as Growlers. And Nathan Mills is the name of some nobody coward who stumbled into a social gold mine. I was being indoctrinated not into a cult, but a cool brew club: a select group of buddies who brewed beer from scratch in each other's apartments every other Saturday. They invited friends over to drink the dregs of their previous batch while they brewed new stock in the kitchen. They called the parties *Cleansings*. It took most of my concentration not to let slip to the boys that Cleanses might be a better grammatical fit than Cleansings.

Knowing I was newish in town and Dennis-approved, they had all pitched in to buy me my own brewing tackle. They taught me the brewmaster's craft that afternoon and they were all so welcoming and unguarded and huggy. The guy on the couch was their friend Pete, a bartender down at one of the swankier Vancouver nightclubs. He loved the Cleansings, but found the early start times hard to handle. He would go into work again that night to drink on the job, get hit on by intoxicated women in skimpy dresses, and make six times my daily pay for three less hours of work.

Dennis and I fell out of the Cleansing drunk and hungry. He suggested we pick up a boatload of sushi and rent a couple of movies. I hadn't tried sushi before and Dennis was enjoying showing me the ropes. "You just sit back and relax. I'll do the ordering," he said to me at the take out.

Under the bright lights at the video store, we kept ourselves entertained with potshots at each other's selections.

"Are you picking that because you want to, or because of the hype?" Dennis pressed, annoyed by the latest Hollywood epic I'd lifted from the New Releases section. Phonies drove Dennis batty, especially pop culture icons that, in his words, marred our society. "Never mind that Nate, here's a few star-studded blockbusters I think you'll shit yourself over. This one's got lover boy Tom Cruise and I hear the budget was in the hundreds of millions so its got to be good, right?"

"Alrighty. Here's one for you, Den. It has about fifteen of those semi-circle olive branches on the cover," I retaliated. "Says here it won the Saskatoon Film Festival's award for costume design. I don't recognize any of the actors. We might have a Dennis Pick."

My edification in the humanities carried forward into Sunday. In the middle morning Rod biked to my place with his proud plan to treat our hangovers with a rousing ride to Commercial Drive for brunch (I kept forgetting I was not to refer to it as brunch). The Drive, as I was told at the Cleansing the day before, was a funky area of ethnic diversity erupting with art and culture: a hood yet to be yuppified into a blasé money trap like Kerrisdale and Kitsilano. A city planner friend of Dennis's at the party had told me the word I wanted was 'gentrified'. The visual artist and bass player listening in on our conversation told me they liked my non-word 'yuppified' better.

We swung by Dan's Brewing Supplies on the north end of Commercial to pick up the raw ingredients I needed for my inaugural brew in two weeks. The store sat next to an independent brewer called Storm. Afterward we rewarded our efforts with a breakfast cocktail on one of the patios and some of the best people-watching around. All walks of life were out in droves, visiting the many ethnic shops, coffee bars, European-style cafes, Latino and Italian restaurants and alternative stores on the strip. Buskers played music for the crowds as others sat at street stalls selling their handicrafts: paintings, poetry, pottery and jewelry. It was as if Dennis had decided to throw a block party.

A lady wearing a fancy sun hat and big dark sunglasses coasted by us in her shiny BMW convertible (Party Lips 007-51), her boutique shopping bags on display in the backseat. She didn't seem to fit in and Dennis let her know she didn't. "Boo-oooooooo!" Dennis yelled through cupped hands over his mouth. You could tell she'd registered him. I never stopped wondering what message, if any, she took away from the jeer. Had she heard jealousy? Contempt?

"Sad how people let what they own define them. But don't let the Gucci piggy in the beemer fool you," he said, and rolled along about how the street-life was not without its grittiness, how panhandling and daylight drug deals were commonplace in the coves of commotion. "Sketch artists everywhere, dude. This one time I was sitting with a friend on the patio of that Vietnamese coffee shop over there and went inside to use the washroom," Dennis continued. "Down a dark hallway to the back of the place I opened what I thought was the washroom door. What I found was six Vietnamese geezers playing cards with piles of cash stacked on the table and skimpily-dressed women, I'm talking young women, dotted all around them. Oh, dude!" Dennis had the stereotypical Hollywood stoner's laugh, that introspective judder-giggle. He let one out now, slapping our round mosaic table. He loved life being what it was: blatantly abnormal; his beloved 'sketch'.

The sun had only then begun to crest the roof of the building across the street. The borderline of the shadow it had cast retreated from my face, down my body, and into the street. Saturated with the warm glow of a day's new light, I sat across from Dennis wide-eyed.

I MADE A SECOND CONNECTION AT WORK: A PLANT
employee named Bill Thompson. Bill was Plant Manager Ron's
brother, which was the key reason why Bill managed to keep his
job as long as he had. Bill was quite possibly the clumsiest human
the world had ever boasted. He'd earned himself the moniker
Spill and the role of company laughing-stock.

I took on an oddball, unspoken kinship with the man they
called Spill, an empathy stemming from having attracted one
lone friend in a city of a million people and my poor track record
at the Help Desk. We were both oafs in our own right. I had no
daily contact with Bill Thompson but I started casually gleaning
information about him from co-workers.

According to Khina in Accounting (a sexually-charged East
Indian woman who had an innocent crush on me), Bill was
neither fish nor fowl nor mollusk at Briscoll Inc. Khina, fifty
years old and mother of four, preferred to eat at her desk and
one lunch hour had welcomed me into her office to share her
homemade pakoras and a chat. "Bert, Ed, Douglas and the rest
of management ridicule poor Spill for costing them money in
delayed shipments and customer dissatisfaction. He can cause
quite a stir," she said in her lively charming accent while making
me up a plate of food. "Those foolish plant boys scorn Spill for

production delays and for cleaning details. But nobody dares do it with big sexy Ron around," she added, winking and passing me prideful dollops of her savoury-sweet mango chutney. I later discovered Bill's fellow blue collars excommunicated him further with hateful rumour-mongering about his home life. I didn't understand why the others couldn't see his klutziness as endearing and just accept him. Treat him like one of the team instead of spiting him nonstop.

A call had come into the Help Desk so I thanked Khina for her time and her scrumptious fare. "Come up and enjoy my curry in a hurry anytime, love," she'd said friskily and winked me off.

Bill would continually pee everybody off by knocking over something full. On our way to a concrete waterproofing seminar the following Saturday in his Toyota Camry (Beach Sand 310-55) Bert told me about the time Bill had spilt the entire contents of one of the three main mixers. "Forgets to activate the backup safety valve on the main drainage spout, brakes for lunch and dumps nearly seven thousand dollars' worth of product onto the warehouse floor. Mess took days to clean. A day in the life of Spill Thompson," Bert said shaking his head in remembrance. "The loser cost me four sales."

At the seminar's lunch intermission, Bert went on to explain how Ron threatened to leave if upper management canned his brother and because in the eyes of Briscoll ownership Ron was the best plant manager in the business, they backed down. "I beg to differ. Stupid Ape," Bert added before continuing on with how Ron's hand was forced into demoting Bill. Labeling detail for three months, a post typically reserved for a female student worker. The rest of the plant had a field day taking Bill to task.

Bert dropped me off at five that evening. "Big day Monday. We're spending the morning teaching the other sales reps the material from today. Come in fresh," he said and sped off.

"OK then. You have yourself a good night too," I mocked to open air.

My takeaways from that sunny Saturday in the conference room at the Airport Holiday Inn:

1. **I didn't get paid a cent for the torture of today, which I**

am required to relive on Monday.

2. Bert, though an elite jackass, knows his concrete cold, and keeps the cleanest car interior in the league.

3. Water is a tenacious shape-shifting butthole that will always find the point of least resistance to destroy everything you build.

4. Poor, poor Bill.

Ron was always vouching for Bill and taking heat for his fumbles. He was a stand-up guy, a true brother, and conceivably guilt-ridden. Few at work were wise to it, but Bill and Ron once shared the same placenta. A condition had developed in the womb called Twin-to-Twin Transfusion Syndrome, where essentially one twin robs the other of blood supply. The recipient twin grows large and the donor twin becomes small and anemic.

I sourced this information from Ron Thompson of all people. After receiving outlandish natter about Bill's personal life from other coworkers ("Spill wastes his paycheck on four-to-five prostitutes a weekend," chinwag coming from the plant dickheads) I had stopped asking around about Bill. Also my obsession with a fifty-five-year-old man had begun to weird people out.

Then Ron and I were teamed up in the annual Briscoll Bowling Night.

As per usual, Dennis didn't show. "Don't shit where you eat." (I always felt the traditional line 'don't mix business with pleasure' more palatable.) Easy for him to say. Unlike Dennis I had very few places to defecate socially.

The alley was lit fluorescent purple with black light. A billion flecks of lint glowed on my ratty navy golf shirt. Something was in the air and the drinks were flying. Everybody was wasted; you got that feeling somebody was going to kiss some body they shouldn't. A popular bone of contention at those Briscoll events was how at the end of the evening the most senior staff member on hand would inspect the drink tab and decide whether or not Briscoll Inc. would be footing the entire bill.

After four trying gutter balls in a row, on the seats behind the scorer's table Ron was teaching me a better handgrip when

I thought to ask him, "Where's Spill?" I'd heard the derogatory name for his brother so many times that week that it just slipped out. I looked up at Ron guiltily to address his displeasure. But the fluke apostrophe-ess on "where's" had saved my life and made it sound conceivable that I'd drunkenly slurred the ess before saying "Bill". Thank God. Big Ron dwarfed me, palming a sixteen-pound bowling ball and making it look like a gumball from the candy machines over near the alley arcade.

"Bill usually skips these Nate," Ron said. "He's at home with his lady friends."

"Lady friends?"

"That's what I call 'em. I'm always razzing him about his romantic comedies. Absolutely loves 'em. Pounds off two or three at a time while I do the crosswords. I do not get it," Ron said, looking out over the string of clamorous lanes with a smile for his quirky brother.

The two were born at home in Prince George during a massive snowstorm that crippled the town. The Thompsons' family doctor, William Balsdon, braved conditions to reach their mother and deliver her pressing sons. Ron appeared first, plump and healthy. Bill came second, deficient and struggling. Dr. Balsdon, quick on his feet, constructed a makeshift manger from cotton balls and a small shoebox and kept Bill incubated through the night by resting it on the oven door. "Slapped him down there on the stove like a turkey. All of 'em thought he'd die in the night," said Ron. Bill survived the night and every night since.

Ron told me all of this between turns and all while getting hammered on the beer. We never had a bottle go empty without full backups by our sides. It was the drinking equivalent of lighting your next cigarette off the dying one in your mouth. The boozing, my relative scoring improvement under Ron's tutelage, and him having had no one to share Bill's story with at Briscoll, set the stage for an upheaval.

I learned about the boys growing up together in the north. The mischief they got into. Though they started off identical, the two looked nothing alike. Where Ron was tall, sturdy and handsome, Bill was short, spindly and plain. The faces held no more clues to their fraternal twinning either. Bill's features were round and lazy, his thin eye sockets the shape of almonds. Ron looked as though he had been carved from stone, with eyes wide and round like untapped walnuts.

Their differences lay not only in the physical. Bill came away from the womb with Attention Deficit Disorder and a debilitating speech impediment. He continually fumbled his words with a heartrending stutter and in the same manner each time: starting a phrase stuck on the first word, revving it like a race car in a starting grid, and then abandoning it for another. When we later met, I said my hello and Bill replied: "Ni-ni-ni-ni-good to meet you." Ron told me they had tried everything to fix it. "It doesn't help—with everything, you know, at work. It's hard."

Ron's telling of their backstory derailed when Khina yelled something over about how hard Ron shoots his big balls down the lane.

Ron was always extra nice to me after that night. We'd high-five whenever we crossed paths at work, just like we had done after strikes and spares at the bowling alley.

It was a sunny day, and I had joined Bill on the picnic table where he ate his lunch every dry day. Ron was mostly too busy eating on the run, so Bill ate alone. His eyes were hidden under the Vancouver Giants baseball cap he wore and his face was flush around the mouth. He was absorbed with picking labeling glue off his hands. At first I struggled with his speaking, but eventually my apprehension let go. There'd been another accident.

"I wouldn't stress it. Ron got it on ice right away. They reattach those no problem these days."

"Thi-thi-thi-thi-thi-maybe so. "

"It needed to be his middle finger. Harry's a dillhole anyway."

Bill appreciated the laugh. There'd been a hullabaloo that morning at tank #3. A batch of Vibra-Coat 2000 (Tropical Itch 761-11) had been readied for mixing by Harry and Bill. Next steps were to fasten the heavy metal lid to the tank and start the mixer at the control box—tasks they'd all performed innumerous times.

Safety regulations required each man to hook the lid onto the latch in front of them, clear their hands from the opening, make eye contact with his counterpart, call out to the other 'Set!' and fold their latches down in unison to seal the tank. The task had become so second nature that the boys had started dropping measures from their routine. Most notably in this case, the 'Set!' and eye contact parts.

Harry had had a fit of three sneezes, so his hand hadn't quite cleared his latch. He'd tried to call out to Bill, who was faced downward for the entire sequence, but it'd been too late.

"Spillaaaaaaahhhh!"

A healthy portion of Harry's index finger had been lopped clean off and was adrift on the surface of the paint amid swirls of blood.

Ron had easily fished out the digit and had driven it and its owner Harry to the nearest hospital. Could it have happened with anyone besides Bill? Tough call. It hadn't before (and never did again). End story: providence returned the top two-thirds of Harry's index finger to its rightful place, with only limited nerve damage. Moving forward, any time I spoke Vibra-Coat 2000 to a customer I had to fight back the tag line, *So thick you can float a finger on it!*

Now after sizing me up some more, Bill told me that Ron had been protecting him from harm his entire life—from the kids in the schoolyard, from a violent sawmill dad at home, from the crews in the work arena. He confided that Ron could be overbearing at times. Bill loved his older brother of two minutes, and regardless of the smothering was proud of him and wanted the best for him.

After that, Bill and I became work buddies. We ate lunch together every chance we could. Though Harry had been a prime menace to Bill over the years, Bill had only worried for Harry's wellbeing that day known thereafter as The Finger F-Up. In spite of his encumbrances, Bill was a selfless, acquiescent man with a steady heart. He was an inspiration to me.

MY SUDDEN SOCIAL RISE WAS PARALLELED BY A promotion at work. At the start of that hefty year, management made me the Outside Sales Representative of our coatings division, citing my growing product knowledge and the rapport I'd nurtured with co-workers and customers alike. This was a decision they would regret down the road. Management also decided to cut the cost of outsourcing the production of our corporate newsletter by making me Chief Writer-Editor of the four-page rag. They cited two well-received articles I had written in the last issue as grounds for this move—a decision they would regret even sooner.

The unspoken reality was that nobody else wanted the position. I on the other hand was thrilled to leave the throes of the Help Desk—minute-by-minute demands of rude, panicky callers that converted my office into a compression chamber. There was also an increase in my salary, which, after taxes and increased hours logged, remained at a steady twelve bucks an hour.

Eager to succeed under the watchful eye of bosses, family, friends, and self, I focused every effort on the business of coatings. I gorged myself on paint; convincing myself it could be stomached. Off the hop, Bert pulled me under his wing and taught me the keys to effective selling—his 'drill bits'. He thought the world of his calling.

"Planet earth is driven by sales. Each person in this place, in this city, owes their jobs to us, the facilitators. Without a purchase order, the plant monkeys have no product to produce, the lab fish have no tests to conduct, the old bats in accounting have no money to collect and calculate, the marketing sloths have no project case histories to boast about, and the pages of your little comic book would be blank, am I right? By the way, when is your next bathroom reader coming out?" (Bert disagreed with my involvement in the company newsletter and thought my time was better served boosting territory revenue. He regularly belittled the four-page quarterly.) "And yet, these idiots still insist on calling us conniving and slimy. It's time they wake up and realize the reason their sons have summer jobs picking tobacco is because some hardworking sales rep went out plugging Du Maurier."

Bert projected his passion onto me. Being an impressionable youngster and new to the game, I gobbled his credos like they were my last meal. He taught me how to push people's hot buttons by knowing what they want to hear, and cautioned me about Tire Kickers—sales terminology for the lot who visit car dealerships, peek in the windows, pore over the different interiors, take test drives, ask a zillion questions and are not even in the market for a car. "Qualify these time-wasters from the get-go," he preached. "If you hear 'just looking', or 'checking to see what's out there' or anything that sounds project-unspecific, politely tell them to piss off. We are only interested in the hard-ons; the dicks ready to blow their loads. Am I right?"

I'd recognized Bert himself as one of these flaccid obstructions from day one, with his daily dose of age-worn sexist jokes and negative innuendos concerning my stepped-up role with the corporate newsletter.

The Concrete News was a promotional piece touting the quality and popularity of our products to industry players. Ten thousand copies of each issue were printed for worldwide mailing. I took pride in the reach it had, and put heart and soul into my first release.

Deadline day arrived. The powers-that-be commended my outlay of articles and my bold change in title from the longstanding *The Concrete News* to *The Cure Times*—a play on the industry term 'cure'.

Concrete does not simply dry per se. There is a chemical process called hydration in which water reacts with the cement in the mixture. Controlling the rate of this reaction by manipulating moisture levels, type of cement, temperature, and other environmental conditions, is known as 'curing' the concrete. Cure times are the different times it takes for concrete to set when those variables are at fixed levels. Note: concrete and cement are not the same thing. Cement is actually a component of concrete—the binding element in the mixture.

The deciders happily signed off on the final printing of *The Cure Times*, their cost-cutting dice roll paying early dividends. They remained unaware that my feature article on page three was an erroneous bungle set to ruffle industry feathers. The article showcased Briscoll Inc.'s involvement in the restoration of a hydroelectric dam in Ireland named Foley Falls. The information I'd managed to wrangle from overseas was patchy at best. Our product was used in some capacity, and it produced sought-after results. I'd finished the sketchy piece, but needed a grabbing headline to go with the impressive aerial photograph of the structure. So I settled on dramatic and alliterative: 'Dam Upgrade—Foley Falls Still Standing Strong.'

After the issue's release, Briscoll Inc. was flooded with heated comments from outraged engineers, architects, competitors, contractors and municipality heads, over the outlandish inference that our products were the key reason why the structure hadn't yet crumbled to the bottom of the River Erne. They were especially upset considering that, of the twenty million Euros dedicated to the renovation project, a grand tally of fifty Euros was spent on two pails of Briscoll product—enough to fill a three-foot crack in one of the dam's utility rooms. There happened to be a hundred such rooms.

"I'm sorry the article is misleading. I guess I got carried away," I explained to a British businessman of some title or another who had phoned the office asking for, "the twit who writes the rubbish".

"This is libel my friend. You could serve jail time," he said in the strictest of cadences.

Granted, I was green, but this man an ocean away was not going to convince me that I would be incarcerated for a slip in our newsletter. It was called *The Cure Times*, not the *New York Times*.

"Hmmm."

He sensed the dissention in my voice. It made him irate.

"You want the real story you daft cunt? The blokes used up your little pail of shit and used the empty for a piss bucket. Print that!"

Our CEO immediately released a statement apologizing for the news article, explaining the cause to be an overzealous recruit in the marketing department, and promising that no more copies of the issue would be printed or distributed (meaning the backwash of the print run would be shipped to the U.S. and South America). For my part, I received an afternoon of internal reprimand but kept my post as editor of the newsletter under condition I triple check my sources and provide proof letters, phone logs and e-mails to my lead hand. Essentially I would be babysat.

For a change, Spill was not the company laughingstock. I'm sure my friend was heart-wrenched to hear of my folly, but nonetheless hoped he appreciated the temporary diversion. Dennis, however, lived for these absurdities. He bucked with amusement when the news broke around the office.

"You are too hard on yourself," Dennis started in on our drive home. "This is a gripping piece and the picture is captivating. You added flair to an otherwise sleeper."

"Flair? I printed ten thousand newsletters with a falsified lead story and mailed them around the world. *The Cure Times* is now The National Enquirer of the concrete industry thanks to me."

"Easy boy. Granted, you screw up lots. Remember the time

you didn't open the air valves on those three carboys and they exploded and flooded Terry's apartment with stout and broken glass? Or the time you fell asleep boiling eggs? They exploded that yellow rainbow over the stove, remember? And the fire alarm went off when the pot melted into the burner? Oh man! Didn't even know eggs could do that. Wait, where was I?"

"I don't know, consoling me?"

"Oh yes. The point I'm trying to make is that we are laughing. That's something."

In a passing whimsy I noted Dennis's high protruding cheekbones and fleetingly likened him to MAD magazine's cover man, Alfred E. Newman. "I work in a small Vancouver office and have a mob of European professionals calling for my head!"

"Your humility is a cherished gift in a world of fakeisms," he carried on.

"Fakeism is not a word. You mean falsism."

"Fakeism could be a word. Open your mind."

"To what, illiteracy?"

"Seriously, those ungrateful Irish should thank their Lucky Charms. There is a village under that dam." Dennis spoke feverishly, unsmiling. "A village full of elated people, singing folk songs about the miracle potion from Canada. The magic powder that saved their village from Erne's raging floodwaters, the torrents that would have swept their town down the valley, wiping out generations of people, ending bloodlines, killing clans."

"Alright, that's quite enough."

"You are a hero. The scribe that marks history, lest we forget."

The paint had dried on our friendship, reaching the comfort level at which there is little concern for offending the other, ever.

Dennis also took immense pleasure in the soft steaming patty that management had stepped in with their handling of *The Cure Times*. He thought they had it coming to them. Piling on the work without par compensation, and sending me out to compete with paint's top dogs with a cinched expense account in that heap that doubled as the office errand machine.

"*No* can be a powerful word. You are doing all this extra

work for Bert F. Dickless and Company *for free*. What's worse, it's killing *me* and *you* are all hunky dory with it. "

"I don't mind the work. Been nice if they had given me a bigger raise," I said, eyes held by the tall escalating and de-escalating privacy hedges of Granville Street passing my window. The groomed evergreen buttresses were a prized aspect of my Vancouver.

"Pshaw! Raise or no raise: YOU ARE A SHEEP!" Dennis shouted with love, breaking my spell. "Take the wheel. I finally feel the aneurism coming on."

Impressionable and meek, I didn't think to mind or ever say no, so Briscoll kept ladling onto my plate. The work piled so high that the division between career life and personal life was blurring. I brought work home in the evenings and weekends, and talked coatings both in and out of the workplace. This infuriated Dennis.

"Do you ever stop and listen to your own spew? New rule: No shoptalk outside the shop! Baa for me, sheep. *Baaaaa*! They are squatting over you and taking steamy shits on your forehead and you smile up and hand them the toilet paper roll!" Dennis would say anything to derail my paint industry rambles. And he was right. I was spread with denial. Plus, I was failing miserably at selling Briscoll paint. Lofty monthly quotas, like human potential, were left unmet: my recurring thirty-day failures. The plant guys went so far as to engineer me the name 'No P.O.', as in 'No Purchase Order'. The tag expanded to 'Pinnopio', as it was procedure to pin the purchase orders to a corkboard in Plant Manager Ron Thompson's office.

Yet I clung tightly to that paint torch.

Unfortunately, overwork and breaking Dennis' shoptalk rule at one of his parties cost me a rare opportunity for a date. I dropped in late after proofreading an article for the newsletter. There was always a crowd. Determined to end a longstanding dateless dry spell, Dennis introduced me to an attractive brunette named Paige after priming her with pro-Nate rhetoric.

Paige was threateningly cute and a fine dresser, and I was drunk enough to maintain eye contact. The conversation started smoothly; exchanging names and a couple of jokes for comfortable laughter. Then the easy, inevitable topic of vocation oozed into the conversation, turning a dry, clean start to glop. She explained her job, something to do with autistic children. Most of it was lost on me as I was too preoccupied with the vendible points of fascination I had in store for her. After a courteous pause, without question or comment in regard to her field, I went to work regaling the pretty girl with a bare bones tour of the Paint Game.

Methodically I explained the key differences between mere paint and the protective systems that I offered. After providing this base knowledge, I enthralled with the truth about popular misconceptions in the coatings industry, such as the incorrect assumption that darker tinted paints hide substrates better than lighter tints (in reality your basic white paint hides substrates better due to its higher levels of titanium—the component of paint that dictates opaqueness. The general rule is 'the darker the look, the more paint it took'). I talked about the impact that temperature and solids content have on drying times, segued into a handy metric conversion tip, and for a big finish imparted the overall importance of salespeople in the marketplace. Paige agreed wholeheartedly, politely excused herself to the washroom, and left Dennis's party without so much as a courtesy wave.

Dennis and I shared a bottle of homebrew while the party dwindled. He took rapturous delight in telling me what Paige had said to him on her way out the door. "Dennis! He's like listening to paint dry. Tell your friend Benjamin Moore thanks but no thanks." Yet my fervour for the paint industry had sand castle stability. If Dennis's taunts were the eroding breeze, my low sales numbers were the flooding tide. Pressure from management to increase dipping revenue made being a coatings activist ever harder to bear. I looked to excuse my shortcomings.

Excuse #1: Transportation. My work mobile was the pioneer of the mini-van; a boxy lemon with four bald tires, loose brakes and three hundred sixty thousand kilometers under its belt. Averse to leasing me a respectable car that I could not afford on my own, the company repainted the rust-bucket a bright white, stuck each side with a corporate decal, and called this middle ground. Their paint job gave the van a sadness shared by old people who wear clothing unbefitting their age. Engaged, the van made a hellish racket, loose parts rattling together in percussive hysteria. It had the contour of a deep freezer but sounded more like a thresher, leading me to park creatively—or where unavoidable, be ill with shame.

Excuse #2 (a): I was expected to save on shipping costs by personally delivering product to job sites. Often times I would befuddle the onsite paint crew by first unloading the shipment and then inspecting the building, asking them questions about their approach and giving them technical advice on use of the product. They'd listen, more or less, confounded as to why the delivery guy was taking such an active interest in the outcome of their project when the rest of them simply dropped off the buckets and asked for a scribble.

Excuse #2 (b): Deliveries were broadened to include generic office errands. They'd say:

"On your way, could you pick up WD-40 for Ron in the plant?"

"We need copier paper."

"Nate, the employee washrooms are plumb out of toilet paper."

Excuse #3: My baby face. Born five weeks premature after my mom induced labour with an innocent dip in a cold lake, my looks, height and weight never caught up with my age. In my collared work shirt I looked like the junior member of a golf club. Aged contractors struggled to see past my boyishness to trust my advice, or simply lacked the humility required to accept guidance from a much younger man. The few customers I convinced to use the products rarely adhered to the application instructions I imposed on them. Miserly pig-headed painters either wanted to cut corners in order to save a buck, or didn't appreciate coaching tips from a youngster.

Excuse #4: Money. It didn't motivate me enough. Dennis had taught me to feel rage when considering the whoredom of society's consumption. Another of Dennis's credos: *Stuff bad*. But to be a money-hater, I found, you must also be a spendthrift. Your cause inevitably cancels itself out by forcing you to concentrate harder on money and your spending in order to get rid of it, but still get by, thus putting the almighty buck back on the very pedestal from which you shook it down. It's exhausting. Flat out: monetary wealth is an all-consuming, ever-losing battle at every level.

Excuses were easy to come by, but candour forces me back to the truth: I sucked at selling. More specifically, I lacked the conviction for Bert's crap-or-get-off-the-pot Hard Close. Without the guts to plant an ultimatum on clients, my pitches waned and purchase orders were left unsigned. Potentials rarely called back. If they did, they had left something behind, like sunglasses or a cell phone. As a result, my job satisfaction was buckling under the squash of an impossible workload and lowly year-end figures.

The height of my disenchantment and subsequent downslide can be definitively linked to a television commercial for *Imodium AD*—a popular diarrhea suppressant. One night Dennis and I found ourselves watching a pale boney white man gangling in a hot tub on TV, a man so slight it appeared he was gripping the sides of the tub so as not to get blasted out by the jets. Two toned, busty women in bikinis—the prescribed blonde/brunette combo—saunter into the steamy water on either side of him. The women flirt with the hot water to get his attention, cupping it in their hands, releasing it over their hair and down their necklines into deep cleavage. The brunette sexily bites her bottom lip and asks the man his occupation. He straightens his back against the whirlpool wall, protrudes his narrow chest, and proudly exclaims: "Ladies, I sell paper." The women ooh and aah and nestle in under his shaggy armpits. Cut to a product shot and a spokesman challenging viewers not to let diarrhea ruin their day. The scene is then back on the paper salesman who breaks loose of the women and jumps the side of the tub, holding his stomach and racing for the nearest bathroom for a wet-go on the toilet.

"Oh my God, that guy is you," Dennis said after blowing out a spray of *Storm Pale Ale* from his mouth like a surfacing beluga.

He rolled around his shag carpet, laughing hysterically.

I did not debate him. The hot tub dork was me. I spoke of paint with the same verve as this farcical paper salesman.

Later that same night, in the quiet reflection before sleep, I whittled a master plan that would, in the words of Dennis, so number my f'n days. It was simple: Act on my daydreams. Save diligently for a backpacking trip to Australia, and discover out there my lot in life here. My sand castle fervour for the paint game had finally been washed out. I slept like a lump of wet sand that night.

ON THAT SOCIAL ROLL OF MINE THERE WAS ALSO A
girl. *The* girl. The one I'd anguished over since high school, the
embodiment of the impossible. A great deal of credit for the
untouchable Nikki Teyber and I getting together goes to Dennis's
faith in my worth, plus an open liquor policy at my Croatian friend
Anita's wedding reception. And to me, for uncharacteristically
rejecting Dennis's advice.

"It looks like a flowery ticket to hell," Dennis groaned from
his sofa cushion after pulling on a joint. Trying not to exhale his
toke with the words, he sounded like he had been winded by a
punch in the gut.

"The lace detailing adds a touch of class."

"Am I reading this right?" he continued, blowing out smoke.
"The reception is in a church basement?"

"They host all of their events at the Croatian Centre. Nikki
Teyber will be there," I added in dreamy contemplation. Dennis
had already been subjected to my Nic rapture. He simply told me
she sounded like any other small town head case.

"Fuck me. You're not thinking of flying back for this shit
show? Huh? Bunch of judgmental hicks sizing you up, sucking
the air from your tires to pump up their own," said Dennis. Then
in his best Tennessean accent: "Boy oh boy, sounds like a real

small town hootenanny. Are you takin' a cousin or can I be your and-one?"

"A lot of my friends will be there." Nic would be there.

Dennis was from the St. Thomas of Manitoba, and although he never had much to say about growing up there, I sensed it had been a struggle for him, too. "It's your money you're throwing away. Just do me this favour. Do not, I repeat, *do not* bring back with you some unwise St. Thomas slapper."

I flew home for the wedding not so much in support of Anita the bride, but because I knew Nic would be her Maid of Honour. I was no better off on the plane having flown once before. Fear transfixed me once again, to the gratification of my seatmate.

Then, while driving my dinky one-way rental car towards St. Thomas, winding and bobbing through the countryside on Highbury Road past Kettle Creek and Spon's Flats, homesickness for the area crept up on me. This is actually a pretty nice place to be from, I thought. Right then I made a promise to myself never to be one of those who blame their small town for being what it is. Happenstance, not St. Thomas, gave me my hard go of it here. Suddenly I came to grips with the notion that trouble lurks in every town, small or big, and it's just that some offer more hiding places than others. I turned up the volume on the local classic rock station and cleared St. Thomas city limits.

My eyes were trained on Nic for the entirety of the ceremony, a ninety-minute religious yawner performed entirely in Croatian. Only Nic could make that puffy green dress work. When I reached her in the basement receiving line, she greeted me with a tight arm-over-arm-under human sash of a hug. My short suit coat sleeves bunched to my forearms behind her back as I took in as much of it as I possibly could. Her curly blonde hair tickled my nose and her ample chest squooshed into mine. She told me how great it was to see my *dirty ass* again and how different I seemed.

Anita extended her arms in the same fashion as Nic, wanting

a heartfelt wring on her day of days. I met her hands with mine and pulled them back between us, gripping and bobbing them as I leaned down and kissed them in a grandfatherly way. There was no chance I was going to let Anita alter the crease Nic had left in my clothes. Nor muddle the smell of the perfume she left behind or steal any of her body heat still warming my upper (and lower) half.

"Vancouver has been good to you Nate," Anita said, recovering from my wintry gesture. "Don't you agree Nic?" she added, looking at her Maid of Honour with loaded eyes.

"Oh fuck yah," Nic joked. "You play your cards right Nathan, we'll be suckin' face by last call."

Classical eloquence begot Nic. In stark contradiction to her wholesome beauty, she brandished a bowling alley mouth with cursing as central to her vernacular as strikes to a perfect game. I loved the contradiction. If provoked, even the cutesy Australian koala can make short work of digging a trench in your face.

True to her word and loaded on lemon gin, Nic asked me to dance one of the last slow jams. Near the end of the song, she whispered, "Aw fuck it," and laid one on me. The kiss, slaphappy but impassioned, caught me off guard—one can never be fully ready for the culmination of ten horned-up years. Sure we were plastered, but neither one of us would be urinating in our family laundry hamper or passing out in the tube slide at our neighbourhood parkette, which meant this kiss counted.

We danced the last three songs as though they were one. Inharmoniously necking, looking as though we were slurping poison from snake-bitten lips. The last tune faded out, and as was tradition, the DJ asked the congregation of four hundred to rise for the playing of the Croatian national anthem.

Lost in the moment, Nic and I continued dancing and sucking face as the opening verse to the stately Lijepa Nasa Domovino resounded over the loudspeakers. Of the throng of people standing at attention, many were visiting from the motherland or were first-generation immigrants. Difficult to put a number on how many of them were appalled by our disrespect for their heritage. Poor Anita had to scurry out onto the dance floor in her white parachute to pry her munjy-cake friends off one another. There were glowers. Later that night, walking Nic home from the after-party, I lamented for a fifth time the uproar—backed by Croatian slurs—we'd incited at the hall. "How could we do that? All of our friends are Croatian! Name one that isn't.— Fine, Troy. There's one. And who's to say he's not a quarter? His grandmother does look Europ...."

Nic halted my course by drawing my eyes to hers, their warm hazel alive under a streetlamp. In the tight white T-shirt and denim she'd changed into, Nic looked more the high schooler I had longed for.

She smiled her wide, toothy smile. "Fuck'em Nathan. Why be a dead horse?"

I succumbed. We had definitely become a work in progress.

Luckily, I had come to my paint epiphany before the Croatian anthem ruckus with Nic—or I would have blown it with spirited talk of coating mil thickness and the infamous Roller versus Sprayer debate.

The very next morning Nic called the house. She just had to see me.

Poof, hangover gone.

We went to a familiar hotspot, The Upper Deck (incidentally the sponsor of my dad's slow pitch team) for what everyone calls the Deck Brek. The tavern bumped on Sunday mornings, which meant we would be seen.

She had her hair pulled back in a purple scrunchie, showing off her perfect little ears. I sat there eating the tastiest food I had ever consumed and dreamily listened to farfetched nonsense.

"I mean," she said, taking a slurp of sugary coffee with last night's lips. "Fuck. How do I put this? I always had a thing for you. No, seriously. Something was always in the way. You mostly." We laughed together. "I mean, you're still a spaz. It just seems to fit you now. You know? Can't believe you of all people just picked up and moved to Vancouver. Fuck man."

We sat quietly for a while.

"What? Stop looking at me like that ya shithead." Nic lifted her coffee cup above her shoulders and pointed into it for the waitress across the room to see.

"I've had a thing for you, if you can even call it a thing, for like a decade now," I said.

"I know."

Nic still lived with her two younger brothers and her parents in a big house with a yellow felted pool table, a big-screen TV, and a two-car garage. The only time I'd been there was a grade eleven party she'd thrown in her parents' absence. The one where I did not, on my way to the upstairs toilet, go into her dark bedroom to feel the firmness of her mattress and sniff her pillows. The memory of which did not become setting for many future masturbations.

Her father worked at the big Ford plant outside of town and spoke only when spoken to. For this I always thought him tough and simple. I also thought he was dumb-lucky for marrying a woman who aged as slowly as a turtle and looked identical to her daughter. Strangers would guess "older sister" more often than "mom". The two of them together filled up any room, barn loft, or auditorium with jealousy and boners. Nic's brothers Brian and Todd hadn't suffered any from their mom's genes either. "Handsome boys, and good little baseball players," people would say in town.

Nic insisted she be the one to drive me to the airport that night. I merely told my mother that a friend was coming to get me.

"Hello Mrs. Mills," Nic said at the front door. Her Trans Am (Fireball 672-22) grumbled behind our family car, a faux-oak-trimmed Caprice Estate station wagon (Butterscotch Ripple 455-44).

"Hi, Nikki?"

"Is Nathan packed and ready?"

"Yes?"

Caught off guard, my mother did a poor job of masking her sudden surprise and eventual delight. Her son had never had a girl around the house—and now this purring kitten with the sports car and the bosoms that wouldn't quit. Though it was a work night, Mom stayed up late to ring me in Vancouver for any dirt on Nic I would give up.

At the airport I experienced the sheer delight of being that guy seen off at Departures by a teary hot girl.

"Tell your Vancouver bitch it is over," Nic said, kissing me at Airport Security.

I laughed at the sheer preposterousness of her demand. Dennis's squirrelly face was the one that popped into my head as I assumed the starfish position for the detector wand. After, in a personal joke as I collected my keys and coins from the scanner, Khina's pudgy face replaced Dennis's to give me her up-down look followed by a slow wink.

From there, a four-month long-distance relationship persevered. My phone bills were out of this world high and I would have paid triple for the privilege of those three-hour nighty-nights spanning two time zones. "I miss your scrawny ass so fucking much," Nic would remind me over and over again. "I fucking gotta get out of this shitberg of a town."

On her first visit to Vancouver Nic was spellbound by the city, especially the Kitsilano area in summer. Roads into Kitsilano ran downhill as the land descended to greet the water. Guarded by hills to the east and the Pacific Ocean to the west, it was naturally divided from the rest of Vancouver, a place all its own. Kits was regarded as prime real estate for its beachfront views, trendiness and proximity to the downtown pulse. Nic wanted to spend the rest of our days there. Personally I thought it a yuppie pit of emptiness and despair where humility went to die: a plastic community beleaguered by materialism. Starbucks their official beverage supplier. But I didn't want to let an elephant into the cab of Dennis's truck (on loan).

"Gawd! If I ever get that fat, you have permission to shoot me in the fucking face," Nic said as she stared at a morbidly obese man driving a motorized cart down the boardwalk. Her snobbery was undercut by her short blue skirt. "I bet you that Paki took the long way," she'd also said of our East Indian cabbie the afternoon we'd had to leave the truck parked, both of us daytime drunk. *Nic is so raw and underexposed, like a baby turtle taking to the ocean,* I mused in my stupour, enjoying her first cosmopolitan steps in those heels that forced her calves to work tight.

The way Nic smiled, looked to the ceiling and shifted her eyes from side to side when trying to remember a thought or a name enchanted me. She wasn't frustrated, but rather amused at how thoughts can be so fleeting. Her uncanny ability to misquote the commonest of proverbs and sayings was beyond adorable, and the shock value she incited with a well-timed F-bomb in front of strangers, priceless. She even flipped the bird in the masculine style, with thumb out. Hot.

We Made Love officially on our last night. She had bought a silky nightgown and imitation pearl earrings for our first time together. It all felt very adult. And the sex was, well, ill-at-ease, with the fitful choreography of battling monkey tribes. As is the way with simian warfare, there stood to be only one winner in that dim bedroom, and I was it—over in a burst of grunt-snort-pant. Again, we were a work in progress.

Living apart was torture at its purest. So Nic decided to make the big move west. I made dinner reservations at a nice Greek restaurant I couldn't afford for the night she landed to stay. I also paid the outrageous parking fee for Dennis's truck at the airport in order to give her a proper welcome rather than looping round Arrivals.

Waiting at the gate for Vancouver Nic to appear, I felt the clean neon light heighten my ecstasy. I smiled dumbly at everyone within reach. *Hey there frazzled woman with the five young children giving you fits while you wait for your husband who was forced to work up north. Ain't life a happy song? I could tap-dance around this indoor fountain. And you there, sorrowful travelling businessman whose wife left you for the handsomer neighbour and took the kids down the street with her. Here's an ear-to-ear variety smile for you. Cheers to life, brother.*

"Unreal," I said aloud to myself for the third time since leaving the truck. Nic had emerged from Baggage; she sort of just came to be, like a divine spirit lugging two heavy suitcases. Her eyes were fixed on me, pocketing tears yet to spill over. My eyes never left her face, not even for a casual peek at those idyllic rounds in her snug button-up. I was waiting for Nic to acknowledge her atypical show of emotion. A tongue waggle, an eye roll, something to say, "Yah, I'm overjoyed, f-off." But her demeanor remained in check, eyes trained on me like the pointed tips of a pair of swords.

"The fuck I let you talk me into this for?" she said, putting the handle of one of her bags, instead of her body, between my outstretched arms. "Couldn't pick a worse time for this. My dad's in bad shape. My mom is a fucking wreck! Brian is sooner or later going to knock up that trollop Andrea if I'm not there to talk some sense into him. My grandmother could go any day now.

"I had a good job," she continued in the truck on the way to the restaurant. "They were good to me. I have no friends here. None. I'm so broke. What am I going to do for work out here? I have nothing. Those two suitcases, that's it. The fuck was I thinking?"

They sat us at a candlelit table. I ordered a Greek beer under recommendation from our kind waiter Mitko. Nic ordered water without looking up at him. We searched our menus.

"I should have thought this through. All this garlic on the menu," I said, trying for a romantic spin.

"Oh pullease, Nathan. I think we're past the point of worrying about rotten ass." Man did she ever look good in candlelight.

To the south of St. Thomas, before plots of farmland take over the landscape, sprawls the St. Thomas Psychiatric Hospital. The Psych is a titanic 460 acre compound that takes ten anxious seconds to drive past, including its road signs warning drivers not to pick up hitchhikers. Built in the thirties, the facility's cultured stone buildings—some constructed with iron bars on the windows—serves everyone from the clinically depressed to the criminally insane, and are lightning rods for the imaginative misunderstandings of children. Snickering doctors with hunchbacks and long noses and hairy ears, big needles in their pockets, roamed the hallways past dim roomfuls of bubbling beakers, head-high pill bottles, and naked screaming patients shackled to stone walls or electrodes. Patients who could escape during a thunderstorm and hitch a ride to your house and eat your family cat Bixbee, leap through bedroom windows to bite the faces of your sisters Anne and Margaret. That was The Psych to a young me. I mention it now because by embittered end, our relationship would feel like those imagined torture chambers at The Psych.

Nic and I signed up for a two month winter sublet in a tiny basement apartment in Kitsilano. Sure it was fast. And she had underlying issues with abandonment and identity, to match my own issues with intimacy, anxiety and self-confidence. But the place was furnished! We were also deeply in love. And it was the only way Nic could afford Kitsilano's inflated rent—she'd decided she could live nowhere else.

We lived directly across from Kitsilano Beach. In the winter months it was a quiet stretch. The overcast skies blackened the water and greyed the mountains snoozing under caps of white. In summer it became a bright sandy platform for people to see and be seen. Posers from all over the city drove their drop-tops to Kits beach to tote their wares. At first our tiny love nest felt cramped, but it was a happy confinement, like the seat restraints on a carnival ride.

Then the rain came down unrelenting that winter. Determined to clear the air fully and completely, rain fell in drizzles, mists, drips, pours, torrents. The inclement weather brought with it travel advisories as dangerous mudslides creamed the Sea to Sky Highway up to Whistler. Stormy weather seeped indoors as well. I was forced to remember my concrete training: *water is a tenacious shape-shifting butthole that will always find the point of least resistance to destroy everything you build.* Nic and I battled endlessly over the silliest of reasons because we were just too stubborn to concede. Over the remote control. "Yes it's your turn, but a fucking hockey game does not count as one show!" (Nic.) The proper way to cut feta cheese. "It's naturally crumbly. Let it be itself. Put the knife away and just use your hands, please!" (Me.) Procedure for taking eggs out of a fresh carton. "I told you to take them from the middle first. Keeps the carton balanced, Shithead!" (Nic.) Which natural disasters were most destructive. "Try hiding in a basement from an earthquake, honey!" (Me.) Whether or not Mr. Bean was actually mute in real-life. "Seriously, read an article about him. That's why he's so good with the facial expressions. Deal with it! Fucktard!" (Nic.) Best air-freshener flavour. "The lemon smells like fucking douche, okay?" (Nic.) Walking speeds. "You realize you are offsetting what little exercise walking offers. Look down. The ants are pacing us to the store." (Me.) Cott Cola versus Royal Crown. "But the Cott label is so freakishly plain, like it was doled out by some communist state. And it tastes as though those throwaway Halloween caramels decided to take a whiz in a can." (Me again.) You name it, we argued it.

Driving the wedge deeper was the wide variance in our stances on the subject of material wealth. Nic sought to surround herself with top brand names even though the funds weren't there, and she knew exactly which top brands she would buy when her wealth caught up with her taste. Stuck in my head to this day is the memory of her dream car: Jeep YJ (Fireball 672-22) with the vanity plate MUDGRL. Nic was about as outdoorsy as the queen diva herself, Celine Dion. Although majestic creatures like Celine *should* be sheltered from dirty things like sticks, moss, and everyday people.

"You are such a tight wad. Look around you, zero assets. You and your hippie fuck-buddy Dennis," she said, irritated with my way of life.

"My happiness doesn't come from a store. And Dennis is not a hippie, he's a realist!"

For the first time in ten years I saw Nic in a whole new light. There was her uncanny ability to successively misquote the most rudimentary of sayings. It could grate your patience down to a nub. Or how she refused to leave the apartment without a shower, blow-dry and make-up. For the two months I lived with her we never once stepped out for a quick bite or an impromptu walk.

When we were finally out for dinner Nic would kitschify appetizers, calling them 'appies'. She always asked the wait staff for 'plain old Vancouver tap water'. Is it necessary to specify the grade, age, and city of origin of the tap water each and every time you order it? *Sorry Ma'am, this establishment only has the flamboyant, youthful, cherry-flavoured, garden hose water from Saskatoon.* And when tasting my dish, she always took the best bite. The one you savour: say, the fluffy middle of a sandwich, the longest french fry, or the droopy arrowhead of a pizza slice. To boot, I had to be extra nice to our servers on her behalf and pad her ten percent tips behind her back.

For my part I struggled to share my Vancouver with Nic. I hadn't anticipated the sensation of my identity being ripped from me like the badge from a movie cop's breast. The Cleansings were Invite Only; she needed to find a Dennis all her own. Dennis himself hadn't the patience for Nic anyway, always having to challenge her comments and viewpoints whenever we'd get together.

By first month's end we were a miserable pair. Descending the staircase down to our basement enclosure, one storey nearer the centre of the earth, meant feeling every milli-newton increase of gravitational force on your body. Yet the only effect this added downward pull seemed to have on Nic was to make her boobs look fuller and rounder. Unfortunately, I hadn't seen them bare in forever. The whole past week she'd been avoiding me, timing errands with my arrivals. On this particular night in our history, I was returning home from work and she was out buying groceries for herself.

I'd dumped my work bag in the closet, intent on fixing my long awaited dinner, when my older sister Anne called to catch up but mostly to talk about our father's depression. He'd been slipping again. I took a kitchen chair and the cordless phone to the small room opposite our bedroom which was not part of the sublet. It had the floor space of a food truck and was overcrowded with glass cabinets displaying knickknacks from the apartment owner's overseas travel (a surfing kangaroo figurine from Melbourne highlighted the collection for me). Nic and I were instructed not to use this room during our sublet, but its high window was the only one that overlooked the beach and mountains. I had taken to standing on a chair in the middle of the room to eye the scenery whenever I talked on the phone at length or wanted to avoid Nic. The stuffed African vulture with its wings spread in the corner had kept Nic out altogether, so there was also the inviting datum that this nook was the only space in the apartment where we hadn't fought.

The call with my sister ended. With a backstop of sand, sea, and mountain I remained balanced on the chair, envisioning my Dad in his bed fully clothed, shoes and all, staring up at his bedroom ceiling trying to piece together his thoughts. The phone rang again. I smiled weakly. My forgetful sister no doubt.

"Hi." Nic had the calmness back in her voice from before her move. Thank exhaustion.

"Hi."

"This is crazy." The bad reception from the supermarket payphone and the background street noise made her voice sound like it came from beyond our reality.

"I know."

"What are we doing Nathan?"

"I don't know."

Torn apart by the constant warring, we split up officially with one month still left on our lease agreement. It took a phone call from afar—one city block away—to drive it home.

After hanging up the phone I likely went and did as guys do to release the tension that those pesky chicks cause us. Lifted some free weights, crushed a large pizza, jerked-off. I most certainly did not go into the bedroom to groan and wet Nic's pillow with tears of heartache. That's not the Nathan Mills we all know.

We lived out the lease together separated. For an entire month we slept in the same double bed with an imaginary line drawn down the centre; both of us too stubborn to take the couch. While asleep I was still drawn to the warmth and baby powder fragrance of her skin. "You were on my fucking side last night," Nic would heckle.

This is how you break up in St. Thomas. You don't break up like this here, ran my feelings after yet another hooded comment about my manhood. She'd taken to dropping such hints in the apartment to get my goat. "Maybe you'll be better equipped for your next girlfriend." "Maybe you weren't built for a steady girlfriend." "Maybe size doesn't matter." *In Vancouver we embrace the spiritual. We—say—each take a rock deep into Stanley Park and bury them together in the woods beside a gnarly old willow to represent the time we were as one. Then we go our separate ways, only to run into each other later in life. We decide to go for an innocent coffee to catch up. We are both married with children, both at peace. We recall the rocks and for a lark decide to go dig them up. I put a flower in your hair for old times' sake. We make love in the crispy autumn leaves with the carnal knowledge of a lifetime of sexual partners. We come full circle. We go to the seaside and offer our rocks to the deep. We never speak again. That's how We do it on the coast!*

We'd promised to remain friends after we moved out and went our separate ways, but that turned out to be customary lip service. "We'll stay friends" ranks up there with "Every day has a purpose" or "I'm a homebody". Things people say to excuse time wasted.

Part Two

Quick Tips for a Flawless Do-It-Yourself Painting Experience

Step 2:

Reveal your paint by carefully removing the lid. Stir the paint well with a proper stir stick taking added precaution to scrape the bottommost edges where details of pigment can hide.

ONCE NIC DEDICATED HER NEW APARTMENT SEARCH
to Kits alone, I reignited my fiery contempt for the area, renaming
it *Kitschylano* to her cringing exasperation. And Kitschylano was
never rapture for me, but it had had its benefits. Outside of the
summer posturing, the beach was picturesque. Massive waist-
high logs had been cut, sanded and positioned to mark group
territory or to shade faces from the peak midday sun. Basketball,
volleyball and tennis courts were all within a hundred yards,
and within the same distance you could get your hands on some
decent beachfront junk food. We'd had our moments, Kits and
I, making peace amongst the pretension over fresh cut fries and
soft-serve cones dipped in butterscotch. But now the place burned
hellish red in my psyche — a fat pustulating scab on the face of my
Vancouver.

Taught by her lookalike mother to avoid leaning on her
prettiness, Nic was raised a survivor. Determined and organized
she quickly found a two-bedroom unit two blocks up from our
sublet. A female Scot, near our age, was in Canada on a one year
work visa and in desperate need of a co-renter. A day did not
pass without Nic commenting on how in love she was with her
new place and soon-to-be bunkmate, or how she could not wait
to show off her new bathing suit at the beach that upcoming

summer. Her post-breakup posturing was making commendable strides.

True to my own form I put off my search until the last minute, when pressure to find a place before month's end started weighing heavily on me. While Nic poised to deal with our separation in swank and string bikini, I stood at the brink of homelessness.

My whirlwind love affair with paint over, I became willing to devote my time at Briscoll Inc. to my apartment hunt and several hands of computer Solitaire. The Vancouver Sun Classifieds—pinched from the break room—yielded three ads in my price range that I circled in red marker.

Zank in Marpole: m, 750 sf, 2 BR, n/s, n/p, prkg, w/d inc., 71st/Marine Dr., $450 + util.

Keja and Marnie in Grandview Woodlands: 2f, 1400 sf, 3 BR, n/s, n/p, I-net, 101 2nd St. E., near Comm. Dr., $525, util. inc.

Layne in Grandview Woodlands: m, 1000 sf, 2 BR, h.wood, near amen. + SkyTrain, Grandview Hwy N/Clark, $500 inc.

Zank was first to knock himself out of contention. The meet-n'-greet we planned that same evening started off promising—nice building, alright area, very close to work. Zank invited me inside after buzzing me up. He was a tall wisp of a guy with spent eyes mismatching lively movements.

"This is she," Zank said, leading me into a tiny bedroom off the main entrance. "Say boss, where you working?" His tired eyes all at once looked at mine and the area around my face.

At that time in my career, inquiries into my job were met with a wall of paint knowledge. A barrage of tiresome information the asker did not seek out nor deserve (i.e. the level of nap required for rolling popcorn stucco; FYI, 25-32mm works best.). "Briscoll Inc. I sell high-level coating systems for the purpose of —"

But Zank beat me to the punch with his own brand of oblivion. "I ask because I work for the city roads department and I can totally get you on." Zank revealed this tidbit with the zeal of a game show host announcing a grand prize. "They pay twenty-five an hour to fuck a dog. I worked today and did nothing.

Absolutely dick all. You ever drive by a road crew and ask yourself what those guys are doing? We're doing nothing boss. Smokin' butts, shootin' shit, spyin' ass. I ask because I can totally get you on. You know how to fuck a dog don't you?"

It was a struggle to determine which was most odd: Zank's predetermination that whatever one's occupation, working Vancouver road detail was better, or his misstep with the saying F-u-c-k *the* Dog.

"Beauty," I said. What else to say?

We moved down a skinny hallway to the common areas at the back of the apartment: a small TV room, kitchen, and pantry. I knew my square footages cold from working with paint so I was mentally prepared for the smallness of scale, but not for the residual smell of cigarettes from past tenants. The viewing ended abruptly with Zank lighting a cigarette and informing me that he requested a non-smoker in the ad because, "you can't very well have two smokers in an apartment this size".

It was for the best. Zank's place had the subatomic smell of pickling brine. Also, I could never get past the cobra neck tattoo and sabre tongue ring. I do have my prejudices.

New to apartment hunting, I'd erroneously lost an entire search day by placing all my faith in Zank. So I cast a wider net the next day, calling both Layne and the girls. As the phone rang out to the girls' voicemail, I envisioned the spiral Nic would be sent into after finding out I was living with two fun-loving, sexy, open-minded, red- and auburn-haired women. Yes, I was getting ahead of myself again.

"Hi, you've reached Keja [Keja's voice], and Marnie [Marnie's voice], please leave a message at the beep [Keja's voice]. And we'll get back to you as soon as we can [Marnie's voice]. Thanks and have a great day [both voices in shoddy unison, laughing as they speak]."

A bubbly message from two easy-going women, I boldly determined. I avoided leaving a message of my own not wanting to blow it already with nervous rambling. That, I could leave for later.

I called Layne next.

"This is Layne." The words delivered flatly, with no warmth or greeting.

"Hi. I'm calling about the rental?"

"Listen here, it's getting very late in the month and so I need to make a decision on the place soon. I'm only entertaining serious inquiries."

"If I'm anything but serious, I will be curbside come April." The grave words came from deep inside me.

"I'm sorry. Your name is?" Layne asked, relaxing into a lukewarm calm. He had a weathered voice. I dejectedly put him in his late forties, flipped the fat red marker in my hand, and crossed out his ad with the inkless butt-end, creasing an X in the page.

"Nate," I said distantly.

"I'm sorry Nate. I've been jerked around lately. You know there are people that apartment-hunt as a hobby. They go around wasting your time and planting false hope."

"Tire Kickers."

"What?"

"Oh nothing. Tell me about the place."

Layne detailed the apartment. "Near Amenities…furnished… no pets…thirty-five…in remission from cancer…close to transit… clean space…" His recent bout with cancer he skimmed over with the same flat tone as the no pet policy, as if the acronym 'rfc' had been casually placed beside 'np' in the advertisement.

Caught off guard and fearful of intense human emotion, I responded timidly. "Cancer at thirty-five? Jesus that's rough. I'm sorry." I cringed as the ignorant words crossed my teeth. I've always been a bit foot-in-mouth, but I only remember this after the fact.

"It's nothing to be sorry about. The doctors discovered a tumour two years ago, they successfully removed it without a trace, and now I'm in remission and recovering fine. End of story."

I appreciated his bigness in excusing my gaffe.

"Can I rightly assume that you are working full-time?" Layne asked.

I gave him a short four-point biography. Then, unaccustomed to my new stance on paint, I reflexively broke into my corporate spiel: the business, the products and the uncompromising quality.

"Wow! At such a young age? Very impressive." Layne sounded genuinely intrigued, even borderline fascinated. I was concerned for his state of mind. "As for my calling, I'm a trained chef. My last gig was Sous-Chef for The Vancouver Hotel, a four-star kitchen. Proud to say they dropped a star when I left." Layne added: "The chemo forced me out of cooking, but I plan on getting back into the business. And unlike other chefs, I do enjoy cooking at home, so you could expect your dinners to be sorted out."

"Oh, that won't be—"

"Cooking for one is a pain. I pair a succulent duck breast with an aromatic Viognier (I had never heard of it) and then the leftover duck goes dry and the wine sours in the fridge. Food is meant to be enjoyed," Layne declaimed. "You'd be doing me a favour. And my dishes."

I laughed with him.

"But don't get me wrong, I am employed. Working for a friend who owns a landscaping business. My rent's always on time, so don't worry yourself there."

Layne felt it necessary to ease any concern about him making rent each month. Call me hasty, but when I rent space with people I take for granted that they have the means to pay the rent.

"That's good. Same here," I indulged him back. *And for five hundred I expect a roof, running water and a separate bedroom.*

We settled on the following afternoon for a viewing.

"Sounds good Nate. See you then."

I'd acted nonchalant on the telephone but was seriously unsteadied by Layne's offhanded delivery of his illness. The world of popular disease was incomprehensible to me, and triply frightening. My grandfather had died of cancer when I was too young to appreciate the hardship of disease and when parents shelter their innocent children from harder truths. Papa was in bed because he was tired, and he passed on because sometimes people went to heaven early to get the place ready for the rest of us.

I also nitpicked over Layne's arrogance in mentioning his restaurant's rating and his rudeness answering the telephone. My mother had drilled into me the importance of telephone manners; she said it was telling of a person. She could be yelling at us kids at the top of her lungs, but if the phone rang, at the precise second she lifted the handset, to initialize the button hook and activate the receiver, she would stick the sweetest-tempered "hello" into the transmitter. Her hello even had a faint "Mmm" prefix for an added slather of sunshine. She could be working in the kitchen and accidentally blind herself with hot grease, or hack her arm off with a meat cleaver—blood spurting everywhere, vision clouding—but if the phone rang, that caller would get the same honeyed "Mmhello" as the last thousand to ring the Mills residence.

So the viewing with Layne was probably going to be nothing more than a courtesy call. Instead I rang the girls again. And again. By the third call I knew it by rote. *"Hi, you've reached Keja and Marnie. We don't answer because we both are too stupid to operate this ringing device on our coffee table. Much thanks to our landlord who helped in the recording of this greeting. Goodbye mystery caller, tee-hee."*

I also called three listings from a website, www.werent2U.ca, but as it was so late in the month, all three vacancies were spoken for. "Cuttin' her close, dontcha think?" one man added helpfully.

NEXT DAY'S APARTMENT HUNTING CAME SWIFTLY. I reserved the company van to first pop in on Keja and Marnie unannounced, a last ditch effort to nail down their room before seeing Layne. That the girls posted their complete address in the listing I read as a sign that I should do so.

I pressed firmly on the gas pedal and the van's parts rattled in unison as it crawled up the steep street. I felt inhumane to push it, like I was whipping an old horse. Waiting at that first stoplight I imagined the transmission, brakes and motor giving way, van and me shooting backwards down the hill past the office, catapulting into the dirty Fraser in a reverse ski jump, buckets of paint towing me to the silty bottom. I waited for green to turn right, giving the old girl a wide enough gape in traffic to pick up speed. The van had no cassette deck, CD player, or working antenna, but the AM dial provided a fitting soundtrack to the day's dryness. Mostly we kept the radio fixed to the reliable feed of the news station; searching for music stations too often proved futile. But today that hadn't stopped me from prayerfully pressing the Seek button and hoping for something to catch. Something outside French and orchestral stations.

Briefly, I landed an oldies music station and belted out the tunes in celebration.

"You see, I've been through the desert
On a horse with no mane.
It felt good to be
Out of terrain."

After a year of outside sales I was the king of avoiding traffic traps. Slicing our way through arterial blockages, the van and I were jangling down Commercial Drive in no time. As the radio lost its signal and scanned for a new one, I turned down the girls' street looking for house number 121. I counted down the addresses: 211, 209, 207, 205…as AM stations scrolled unsnagged. 1290, 1340, 1410, 1520…

Something needs to catch.

One Two One was a house like any other with windows, a porch and a roof; I was more concerned about dropping in unannounced, and in my dorky work attire. The corporate logo on my golf shirt matched the decal on the van and made me look like an exterminator. Or not even — with my young face I looked more like an exterminator's apprentice. So the house didn't matter. I'd live in an insulated mudpack. I was desperate.

Something has to catch!

Keja answered the bell. She had a distinct style to match the name: long gummy dreadlocks scrunched into a pink bandana, caramel skin tone, symmetrical facial beauty and eyes a telekinetic twist of greens, browns and blacks that made you feel as though you were being mind-read if you stared at them too long. She wore a white tank top with 'Ocean Pearl' stitched across the chest in pink italic font. The letters were stretched by her enticing breasts and the top's sleevelessness exposed the muscle definition in her arms — not a manly bulk but a fine feminine carving. Pink track pants hugged her slender legs down past her knees where they bunched to expose two shapely calf muscles and two bare feet with funky toe rings on both second toes. She subjugated the space around her, embodying the beautiful punkiness of The Drive. This girl could make Nic squirm, I thought excitedly as I seized up with my signature hottie phobia.

"Sor-sorry to pop on in you like thi-this." I sounded the idiot from the get-go.

"That's OK," she said patiently.

"My name is Nate. I left Marnie and you a message on your phone about the space, the room, for lease, for rent. I was in the area checking out the area, so thought I would try knocking or ringing on your door."

"Actually, I'm Marnie." She paused a second to address my bizarre attempt to pin a name on someone I'd never met. "We have not found anyone, but sorry, we are looking for a girl to join us."

She said "Join us" as though she was Grand Poobah of an illicit lesbian sex cult. My imagination shifted to sweaty girl-on-girl-on-girl action but was interrupted by thoughts of Nic's probable glee if she found out the girls had been looking for another female all along. This now was interrupted by thoughts of me sleeping on a park bench in the rain with an empty plastic pop bottle for a pillow and layers of newspaper for a blanket—the scene wet and heavy like an oil painting.

But Keja—Marnie rather—had excused herself and shut the door. My three overlying visions were impelling me to ring the doorbell again and explain to Marnie why I was the closest thing to a girl she could get in a guy. To tell her about the testicle that wouldn't descend when I was twelve. How I required two procedures to pull it into place—manhood nearly eluding me altogether. To give her a list of the multitude of movies and TV programs I've wept to, including My Girl, the ending of Jerry Maguire, and the series finale of Family Ties. To let her know how immaculately tidy I am and hip to lighting the odd scented candle if a foul odour overtakes a room. To present my enjoyment in the occasional bath, my closet addiction to bubble soap and my daily moisturizing and plucking routines. To disclose to her that when I wake up in the middle of the night to use the bathroom, I sit down to pee and get angry when I leave my own toilet seat up and that I sometimes dab off with toilet tissue and that I call it "toilet tissue". To let slip to her that I apply the words "precious", "famously" and "cute" in everyday speech and that I talk with my hands and that my favourite toy as a child was a Cabbage Patch Doll named Freeman Robin. To relate to her in how we both prefer to be spooned rather than to spoon. To admit that I'm mechanically disinclined, have never been in a fistfight and am just about as unmanly as men come.

My emasculating trance was broken by a ruffling of the curtains in the picture window off the porch and an awareness of my regression from humble visitor to trespasser. I slouched back to my laughable ride and gave the house a generous look from the driver's seat. "Out of your league," I said, plucking the newspaper and red marker from the passenger seat to make it official. The newspaper page looked like a ruined ballot, the ill-mannered cancer veteran, Layne, the only candidate without a vote.

Unable to bear another fruitless effort I turned the dial straight to the news station and looped back to Commercial for Grandview Highway North and my appointment with Layne. Commercialites — a salmagundi of Vancouverites — filled the strip in both suit and tie and ripped jean and T, making the most of the gifted weather. Musicians and artists out in full charge staged their inspirations of sound and colour. Stopped at a red light, I turned down the traffic report to hear a man play Neil Young on acoustic guitar. I sang along until signaled to go. I sang the wrong words: eagerness to join in makes me compose random lyrics.

As you move south from the main drag The Drive's scenery begins to change, the people begin to change, and you yourself begin to change. Multi-hued Edwardian buildings disappear to the dilapidation of inner city poverty. Litter blanches in the sun. Steel bars crop up on windows and humanity dwindles, sallow faces reflecting indifference as if these people have climbed into their own shadows to roam. It's a transition similar to leaving a town fair, buzz of activity and joy at your back as you make your way, tired, past blank faces in a dark garbage-strewn lot. Poor souls live in this periphery, forced to watch the festival-goers to and fro. I had rarely found myself in this hollow of Vancouver.

I passed a quiet road. I steered the van underneath a section of SkyTrain tracks, through its concrete footings and striped shadow, then across a tiny railway bridge to the busy intersection of Broadway and Commercial, and realized I had missed my turn. Broadway and Commercial is a scaled down version of the misery and confusion rampant in Vancouver's heroin-rich East Hastings district. It plays meeting-ground for homeless, junkies and prostitutes. Speeding up, I crossed through the lights and used an alleyway—home to three grown men at the time— and doubled back to catch the same green light, thread under the SkyTrain tracks, and reached my left turn on Grandview Highway North. To get to Layne, to get to forgetting, to get gone.

Quietest road ever to be named a highway, I thought as I hit my turn and drove on.

Layne's building complex, at the midway point of the first block, was a two-storey replica of those dumpy freeway motels in the movies: a real pile. "Complex" was the perfect term for this building, as it was pieced together with a mish mash of materials. Stucco, brick, concrete, plywood, particle board, duct tape, tar, and rubber kept it erect. An array of weathered colours made for quite the eyesore: walls faded Paprikash (584-84), trim three shades of Harvest Moon (422-90), water-stained wood (Polar Dim 671-00), rubber patchwork (Starless Night 874-21), and rock-dash stucco (Golden Terrier 798-99). Two square posts built of bile-coloured brick, like decaying incisors, marked the entrance.

The land opposite Layne's building had been zoned by the city for the SkyTrain line. A tall security fence ran parallel to the street to discourage trespassers from its overgrown urban savanna of trees, tall grass, and brush. These gave way to the massive concrete stilts supporting the tracks a stone's throw from the road.

"Keep driving and never look back," I said to myself aloud.

Nic popped into my head as the van bounced over the cracks and potholes of a sinking asphalt parking lot and idled past the lone vehicle in the lot: a rusty maroon Pontiac 6000 with two flat tires. Nic was dressed as a naughty school teacher: black stiletto heels, short grey skirt, white blouse unbuttoned to her cleavage, dirty-blonde hair pulled back in a tight bun, dark-rimmed eyeglasses. Her sparkly white panties peeked out the bottom of her skirt and hugged her behind as she leaned over the ledge of a chalkboard. Written on the board in white chalk were the names ZANK, KEJA & MARNIE and LAYNE. ZANK and KEJA & MARNIE were squiggled out. Nic pressed her heaving breasts against the dusty chalkboard and started erasing LAYNE by following the letters with her wet tongue.

Snap out of it man! Mustn't fantasize about the ex, it gives her power!

Two decks of apartments spread along the back and to the right of the crumbling parking lot in an L formation. Each apartment was accessed from the outside by one of two doors on the ground level; one leading into a ground floor unit, the other to a set of stairs and the unit above. The window eyes on the second floor, the door mouths on the first floor, and the crazy-quilt riggings, made the place look like a scarred head spinning on its neck.

I brought the van to rest in front of 212, beside the crook in the L. A concrete sidewalk with an impressive strewing of flattened cigarette filters and spiny weeds separated the parking stalls from the entrances. There were no signs of life. I knocked on 212.

The door opened to a man shrouded in darkness.

"Hello, Pete?" he said and stuck his skinny hand out into the sunlight.

"Nathan. Layne?" I replied automatically, thinking: what a feeble grip.

"*Nate*, so sorry. Please, come in. Your shoes are fine."

I climbed the steep stairwell behind him noting the pale toothpicks poking out of his beige walking shorts. They occupied little of the leg holes. Does chemotherapy make your leg hair fall out? I wondered. I still hadn't seen his face, but his curly brown hair hung past the neckline of his long-sleeved T-shirt in an admirable St. Thomas mullet.

Layne stepped aside when he reached the top to allow me space. My eye level rose over the last step and I saw her, in all her glory: at that exact moment in Layne's apartment the sun shone through the large living room window sending a ripple of light cascading from immaculately clean planks of hardwood to a big-screen Sony Vega television at the back of the room—their flagship model.

"Any troubles finding me?" Layne asked. He faced me now, and his smile curled up underneath, of all things, a moustache. His yellowed teeth matched the brick posts outside and he had the straight sallow cheeks of a dingo. To go with his beige shorts Layne had chosen thin brown socks spotted with white paint flecks, and his long-sleeved T-shirt was a blue and gold cotton job with **Ram Invitational** stitched to the front above a cartoon ram.

"Actually yes, I missed Grandview and had to turn around at *Broadway*." I wanted to prompt a comment about the hordes of downtrodden living mere blocks from his home.

"Damn shame how far down some of 'em get," he said with compassion, overstepping the first hurdle I'd set.

"I know. It's so sad," I agreed gleefully.

The high ceilings and roominess of the space took me aback, as did the man starting for me from the couch. Hypnotized by the television and first impressions, I had failed to register a third man in the room.

"Nate, this is my friend Mark. Mark lives in the building, don't you Mark?" Layne said in a paternal tone.

Spoken to as a child, Mark nodded, eyes cowering to the floor, yet he didn't have the look of a biddable man. He was Layne's average height but thicker, sleeve of tattoos winding down one arm. Unshaven black stubble, matching black circles around tired eyes, shag of greasy black hair, grey tank top, ripped blue jeans. Mark looked hard. With this strange cowardice, he just wasn't acting that way.

"I'm Nate," I offered along with my hand.

He forced a weary smile and met my eyes for an instant before slumping his back down to the floor, the corners of his mouth following suit. Like a frog's tongue that missed its fly, my unshaken hand recoiled to my pants' pocket.

Layne put his hand on Mark's shoulder. "Mark was just heading out, weren't you Mark? Off you go."

Mark said nothing and left. When I heard the downstairs door close, I made for an innocent joke: "Geez, hope I didn't scare him," I said. I don't scare anyone.

"No," Layne said, laughing excessively. "Poor Mark is just battling the blues. Shall we?"

He first led me to the vacant bedroom at the end of a short hallway left of the entrance. Vintage hardwood floored every room but the kitchen and bathroom. "Thought the guest room could benefit from a little paint," he said buoyantly, pointing to paint props and two buckets of Spector (946-22) tucked in a corner.

The bedroom was bigger than my last three combined and the buckets of sunlight splashing in from the large window and yawning balcony door made the space seem all the larger.

"Is that for when you can't take it anymore?" I said, pointing to the balcony. Bolstered by Layne's response to my first wisecrack, I had tried for another, momentarily forgetting Layne was a cancer victim. I froze up, locked in a type of social anaphylactic shock. *You are the dumbest person alive!* I screamed inside myself.

Layne blew off my comment. "Nah, this is your reading balcony, for when you can't take *me* anymore."

The front's wooden balconies had been lost on me in the exterior's erratic visuals. I stood in the doorway, not daring to step out. The balcony wood's original paint had been stripped by weather and was rotting from exposure; it sagged from the doorjamb as badly as the bags under Mark's eyes.

"After I finish painting the bedroom and the trim in the living room, I plan to lay plywood over this dead stuff and paint the whole thing."

The coating is only as good as the substrate to which it is applied. Business mantras pecked at the backs of my eyes like a ghost typewriter. Covering up dead wood with new wood is not a sound fix either. "Probably not worth salvaging. Too far gone," I said, trying to save Layne from futile hassle and possibly a broken neck.

"Yeah, you're probably right," he agreed distantly, mature enough to heed the counsel of a youngster. Unlike the monsters I tried selling paint to.

While the street was in view, I asked Layne about street noise. He assured me that his little backwater saw limited traffic, and as if on cue, the SkyTrain glided by, its mechanisms muted by digital engineering.

To revive a pocket of dead air, I asked him what 'Ram Invitational' meant.

"Who knows?" Layne answered, tugging on the front. "It's just a T-shirt.

"I have an en suite, so the bathroom in the hall would be yours alone," he continued, motioning our tour forward. "I would only go in on a house-clean."

My crooked look was questioning.

"Nate, the neat freak in me needs the therapy. It comes from years in top kitchens. You'd be doing me a favour."

"I'd be happy to help," I offered, uneasy.

The bathroom was a good size and spotless. Layne also assured me of the mannish water pressure. I hadn't even thought to ask.

"I'd show you my room, but it's a war zone," Layne said, speaking to his bedroom at the opposite end of the hall.

"I'm not bothered," I said, curious why he'd chosen the back room.

"It's not like you would be sleeping in there with me, so, no, not now." He laughed nervously to soften his strange insistence; an awkward though forgettable break in the proceedings as we forged on to the kitchen at the opposite side of the stairwell.

I cook the single man's core five—eggs, toast, soup, spaghetti, sandwiches—so as long as there's a fridge, toaster, and hotplate, my range is satisfied. But it turned out Layne's greatest pride was showing off his kitchen gadgets. He pulled them forward on the counter one at a time, announcing their function: "Chopper... Dicer...Blender...Slicer...Juicer..." They looked dated, yellowing white plastic, rust stains around the metal bits.

"That just leaves the, uh, laundry room. I didn't bring it up on the phone because of, well...ta-da," Layne announced tentatively with all the conviction of a rookie magician. He pulled aside a bed sheet (Baby Basil 254-31), nailed to the doorway at the back of the kitchen with three flatheads, to reveal…a washer-dryer set, and a flock of eight marijuana plants, rich foliage baking under a heat lamp. Layne's Grow-Op. The plants were tipping the bottom of my chin, a veritable jungle for laundry room standards.

"See how I jerry-rigged an exhaust through the ventilation duct?" Layne pointed out, lost in his own craftsmanship.

"That's something else," I coughed out, stunned.

"This is legit crop. I mean, it's on the level. I'm a card-carrying member and sponsored grower for the Compassion Club, a society sanctioned by the government to help the terminally ill with counseling and medicinal cannabis. Due to my health condition, I am legally permitted to purchase and grow marijuana."

I shifted in my shoes.

"I grow for personal and give the extra back to the club. They make the supply accessible to members by selling it dirt cheap. They refer to me as a Home Grower, allowing me to rear up to ten plants, as long as I don't sell any of it commercially." Layne dug into his pants. "See. Here's my membership card."

Dennis's intimacy with Mary Jane had me accustomed to her sights and smells, so any stigma had eventually burned off. Still, I rarely partook. And that was the demand side of the chain. This was the supply side. After hearing Layne's briefing and seeing his credentials, I went from overawed to run-of-the-mill awed. I still simply trusted people if they needed me to.

Layne had left the grow room and was calling after me. I wanted time to inspect the plants and the equipment that urged them to flower. Reluctantly I heeded Layne's call, but not before rubbing a spiny leaf between my fingers.

He was sitting on the couch, which was placed back facing me, and he was wagging a booklet over his head. I walked from the kitchen around the right armrest and sat next to him.

"This book has it all. The Club gives these to their growers."

As I read the introduction Layne took a small wooden box from the coffee table drawer and began rolling himself a joint, breaking up tiny orange-haired clumps of branch and bud and releasing their resin smell into the air. He dropped this shredding into a canoed rolling paper and rocked the weed into itself to tighten. He showed the deliberation of a tradesperson, a musician or athlete who has mastered his craft and approaches it with respectful legerdemain. I watched fascinated, completely distracted from the how-to guide in my hands and forgetting it was even there. "You get the knack after the first five hundred," Layne mused. Then using the joint as an extension of his hand, he waved me to follow through a rear door to a back balcony. Unlike the rickety extensions out front, this one—covered concrete decking built flush with the outer wall—was part of the building's original mold. From front to back the view transformed: transit tracking and ratty overgrowth, to a serene residential imprint of red brick homes and thick leafy canopy. It reminded me of Forest Avenue, the road I grew up on in St. Thomas, with its roosts of black bats hiding in the tall maples.

"You smoke?" Layne offered a puff like he was a television reporter and the lit joint his microphone.

"Not really, no."

"I have sold some of my crop on the side, nothing major, a baggy here and there to friends. There are supposed to be quarterly inspections to make sure we are planting within the permissible limit." Layne chuckled. "A rep hasn't been by here to audit my farm for going on two years. It's still very much a Mickey Mouse operation, run by a bunch of bakers in it for the free bud. Too bad. Many people depend on their medicine, and meanwhile these guys are bungling their deal with the government. I bring it up to say I wouldn't have a problem with you helping me grow and selling some to your friends. There's zero risk because it's all legal crop. I'm not talking by the pound here. You could even give it away to friends or family if you wanted."

Give some to *family*. I was no longer in Ontario, clearly. My face went redder.

"No big deal, just throwing it out there."

"Thanks for that," I managed finally.

Layne drew in another plume and spoke as it sputtered from his mouth. "What else? Oh yes. The landlord Mr. Chin is a finicky old coot. Only does his dealings with me. He gave me a break on this month's rent to do his grunt work for him. Cracks me up. 'Len, dun peek-ow ass-hoe lack bee-foe, ow-kie,'" Layne impersonated, the mimic made funnier with his bloodshot eyes. "I used to share the place with these two Kiwis. All they did was sleep here and boy were they brash. I'm not saying I need a soul brother. I just find it uncomfortable to be on a hi-bye level with the people you share a roof with," he continued, raising his right hand. "If you do rent here Nate, this would be *our* place. Not just me lending it out to you. There's something you don't agree with, we work out an arrangement. Like the hallway trim for instance, I didn't start painting it because I wanted to pick out a colour *with* the next renter."

The viewing was running on so I hinted at excusing myself. On the way out I asked about a small, eye-catching picture of a snowy landscape hanging at the top of the stairs. "What part of the world is that?"

"Don't know. Just a picture is all. Something to cover bare wall," Layne replied. His entire place had a quirky hand-me-down theme. The gimmicky kitchen tools, the consignment furnishings (excluding the Sony), the wall ornaments, the pictures in the living room, the shirt on Layne's back, everything second-hand with no special meaning. The apartment even boasted a macramé owl knitted between two rough sticks of wood. A craft one would expect to find at a flea market or in their grandmother's sweetly scented basement.

"If you will indulge me, I wanted us to say a quick hello to my downstairs neighbour," Layne said, following me out his front entrance.

A little woman, teetering unsteadily on black high heels, answered his knock. The grey gabardine suit she wore—probably the first of its kind, rushed to the racks in a triumph of the woman's labour movement—cried out: "Iron me!" Most of her pale face hid behind large round sunglasses. Her lips were dry and cracked, and filled in with a thick coat of red lipstick applied by an unsteady or untrained hand. A bushy thicket of curly black hair stopped at her shoulders and made her face look like the head of a ripe silky dandelion. I fought the urge to pluck her off the ground, make a wish, and blow the hectic strands into the air. Overall she had the slipshoddiness of a young girl in a game of dress-up.

"Nate, this is Mrs. Holme. Mrs. Holme is a schoolteacher and has lived in the building going on seven years."

"Pleasure. My mom actually teaches grade one back in Ontario."

Mrs. Holme smiled the same faint smile the entire time.

"Mrs. Holme has two kids, Stanley and Cindy," Layne pushed.

After another painful gap of silence, Layne retracted and put a stop on the introduction. "Thanks Liz. Be seeing ya."

Mrs. Holme went back inside without a goodbye.

"She's exhausted after chasing her students around all week long,"

It was Tuesday.

Layne carried us forward. "So, is there anything else you need to know before making a final decision?"

I eased into my top concern: "How can I put this without sounding…? It's just that you are so close to Broadway…"

"Say no more. Honestly, they leave us be down here. I rarely even lock the door."

"Oh God! I mean, good, good to hear."

"Any other questions coming to mind?"

Several I couldn't ask due to their inappropriateness or insensitivity: *What form of cancer did you have? How would you describe the pain? Do they sell baked goods at the Club too, like brownies and tea biscuits?*

"Nothing comes to mind. Guess you've done your job."

"We'll see if I have," he laughed. "Let me say Nate, it was a pleasure meeting you. You seem like an upstanding young man and a good fit."

Layne smiled exuberantly as I bounded over the riddled asphalt and headed west.

On the drive back to *Kitschylano*, the city tempered by an orange dusk, I spun in my head a cross-referencing web of pros and cons:

PRO:	Spacious and clean.
CON:	Looks condemned from the outside.
PRO:	He cooks. He cleans.
CON:	The cancer. Did I want to move into a potentially complex, emotionally-charged situation? What if he relapsed? No way I could handle being there when he got The Call from the doctor again?
PRO:	Nice, thoughtful guy with a sense of humour.
CON:	Fellow tenants, Mrs. Holme and Mark, seem unplugged.
PRO:	Near Commercial Drive, far from Kits and Nic's bikini.
CON:	Near hordes of desperate homeless, far from Dennis and rides to/from work.
PRO:	Onsite laundry.
PRO/CON:	Grow operation. How badly could this end? Was this an after-school special in the making? Then again, if Layne was on the level, there was opportunity to fast-track Australia by making some easy money for a change. And why not? Years of eking out pennies with corn detasseling, blueberry picking, telemarketing and paint selling had piqued my interest in the mythical Effortless Buck. And I'd be a godsend to Dennis and a celebrity within our circle; the hippie Santa Claus, bringing affordable homegrown to the good little party boys and girls.
PRO:	The baking smell. Layne's apartment had had a familiar smell I couldn't place until I thought back to it in the van: Grandma Agnes's house. The air inside of my grandmother's house was an odorous

melody of caramelizing brown sugar and melting butter. Even the bedding had the sweet nose, as though she knew we were coming and stuffed the pillow shams with the same mixing bowl crème. On the other hand, the delectably cloying smell that was pleasurable for a few days was too much for daily living, so I was always comforted by returning to my scentless home.

UNDECIDED: Moustache.

UNDECIDED: Macramé owl.

BIG CON: Occupying the innermost radial of the web was Layne's compulsion to win me over; a frantic desperation that set off an alarm in my head. Layne had conducted himself like the host of an infomercial. *Time is running out. You get the maid service, the live-in chef, the juicer, the dicer. What audience? You say you want more? Alright then, how about unwarranted awe for your tedious occupation? Free ego boosts! What, not enough? Fine then, call in the next couple days and I'll include the laundry room marijuana. Sell it to friends or smoke a bowl with grandma. You'll pay not seven-hundred, not six-hundred, but five-hundred dollars a month! That's only if you have a job that earns you a salary! Some restrictions may apply.*

And that bedroom did not require repainting: a professional, me, could barely discern which walls had seen new paint and which ones had not; while the reading balcony was blatantly unsalvageable. Layne was trying too hard.

Parking the van in front of our sublet, I toyed with the fantasy of kissing Nic hello and telling her I'd found us the perfect apartment. But once inside I saw her prepping dinner, chopping vegetables with petty precision, careful to make enough for only one serving, and I realized just how far we had deviated from that fantasy.

Tight blue jeans and a white ribbed tank top—the brightness of the shirt enhancing the chocolate creaminess of her tanned shoulder—stole my attention. She bit her plump bottom lip in concentration.

I faked indifference.

"You look like shit," Nic offered.

"Good to see you too." I ricocheted off the smelly insides of the fridge as I hunted an easy bite. The past month our insecurities had been transmuted into infantile slander. Two feeble babies unable to nourish their own lives, slinging poop at each other.

"Don't tell me you struck out *again*," she said. "A city this gi-normous and you can't find one bedroom? That's what you get. Putting in the time and seeing as many listings as you can is part and partial to finding the right fit. You are royally fucked now. What are you going to do? Hello? Nathan, this is serious for you. Nathan?" Premeditated smugness is the worst type of pride. Blurting it out like an uncorked bottle of rattled champagne, she had been cellaring this vintage of bubbly for when my predicament looked its most bleak.

I signed a one-year lease with the girls. The apartment is a dream, a punt from Commercial. Keja and Marnie are quite the pair, very spunky, Should be crazy fun. Oh how I wanted to tell her that! And watch her levee of poise crumble into a jealous gush of inquiry: *Where is this place? You and two girls? What kind of a name is Keja anyway?*

"Oh relax," I said calmly, surprised at having no follow-up dig. Looking down at a waxen apple in my hand, I said, "We will both be happy, you in your new digs and as of today, me in mine."

SOLD! I decided to take Layne's offer right there on the spot. My mental spider web had been dusted by a sweep of self-mutiny and what was now a screaming leap of faith.

Nic blushed as she replayed her self-righteous babble in her mind. Spent from a long day, I jumped ahead of her questions and gave her my uncut, sugar-free take on Layne and the Grandview apartment. I tried my best not to look at her fine cleavage and daydream of base jumping down inside.

"Are you fucking for real? Oh my god, you are serious!"

"Problem?" I said, annoyed.

"Are you fucked in the head?" Nic numbered the points on her manicured fingers. "One, this guy sounds crazy. Two, he's offering up his *services*? Have you thought about what he wants in return? Three, he's growing *dope*. Four, psycho neighbours. Five, Broadway and Commercial is a hellhole. Six, uh hello, cancer!" She lifted her fingers to her temples and tapped them against the sides of her pretty melon, imploring me to think.

I *had* been thinking, and coming to the conclusion that there were greater personal and social ramifications to this move than mere lodging. I decided right there in that kitchen that I was at a crossroads in my morality and the move east represented an ideal, a path to enlightenment, a righteous nobility. It meant refusing to turn a blind eye on humanity, taking a stance on what should be valued in our world: benevolence over materialism. Nic could keep her Kits with its haughty ignorance and empty riches. She could continue sheltering herself from the suffering and the desperation. I was now after a clearer focus on life. In a matter of minutes, deciding to move my paltry effects across town had transformed into a grand humanitarian crusade. A crusade of one: easy to organize and no solo crusader gets out of hand, takes a billy stick blow from riot police, gets tear-gassed, or goes to jail.

Fleeing the kitchen before the smell of Nic's home-cooking-for-one took over the air, I excused myself to the bedroom to countermand my earlier list of Cons and call Layne with the good news.

I dialed Layne on a cordless from my side of the bed. He was pleased with my decision. I also said I could get him free paint for the trim by ordering a client sample. I asked his colour preference.

"Ah, whatever you think. It's only paint."

Boy, you said a mouthful Layne. It's only paint, just like they're only T-shirts, furniture and wall-coverings—mere trappings, material nothings, golden calves. Good on you man! I gloried in my new vein of Dennis's wisdom.

Layne asked if I could pay the rent and damage deposit in cash. His landscaper buddy paid him under the table and he avoided the banks whenever possible.

"You're not a con artist are you?" I asked flippantly.

"The first rule of conning: never admit you're a con artist."

"Oh yeah, what's the second rule?"

"The second rule: uh, never con yourself."

Oh that Layne, I thought smiling. In the name of fellowship, I agreed to the paperless transaction and said my goodbye. Nic and her cynicism wouldn't understand.

I put on some music and relished the thought of Nic relaxing on IKEA furniture, sipping her Starbucks, and dressing shamefully provocatively, playing scamp at the uptight martini bars. Flirting with pretty-boy metrosexuals who spend more time at the gym than they do reading. Nic and the rest of her Kits brigade, flaunting their three-hundred-dollar haircuts and their three-hundred-dollar jeans and their three-hundred-dollar handbags and their three-hundred-dollar bar tabs. Make believing it is their birthright to live indulgently, while Nate keeps it real to the east.

Karma Police by Radiohead played at random on the six-CD changer, and I found the anthem to my Crusade. I sang what I thought to be the chorus:

"This is what you get,
This is what you get,
This is what you get,
When you mess with usssss."

I dozed off before song's end.

DENNIS DROVE US HOME FROM WORK THE FOLLOWING
Monday and took the brunt of my exhilaration, just as he had my
sorrow when Nic and I split. It can't be said enough: a primetime
friend is Dennis Zimmer.

However Dennis's attire needed addressing. He was
struggling to look the athlete in an all-grey tracksuit with elastic
bands hugging tight above the ankles and a pair of department
store knock-off cross-trainers called Zoomers. "Lawn bowling
tournament at the retirement villa?" I said, giving his sweats the
up-down.

Dennis had joined a co-ed Ultimate Frisbee Team in pursuit
of a certain person he was fond of and tonight was a league
night. He hated the exuberance of the players and the having-
fun-is-number-one, soft culture of the league. "Dude, I fucking
hate Frisbee. Last week was like a bad trip. We lost by one and
I dropped two key scoring passes from you know who, both
disced right into my bread basket."

"Disced?" I implored.

"Let it go."

"Fine, continue."

"These three douches on my team kept calling out 'That's OK,
Dennis. We'll get it next time.' And once the players on the other

team caught wind of my name, they started doing the same: 'Good effort Dennis. Nice run.'

"The players call the Frisbee 'the bee' for short. 'Pass me the bee!' they scream out. No lay can be worth this," decreed Dennis.

I agreed, as jaded as they come, then quickly changed the subject. I yelled over Dennis's dirty engine. "So the Master Plan, Den. Move east, far from Kitschylano and Nic's mind games. Gain enlightenment through acts of charity. Sell Layne's extra weed and save for Australia. Capitalize on low rent, proximity to Commercial Drive, Layne's cooking fetish and the Sony to live on the cheap. Six months down the line, I give Layne my thirty-day notice and Briscoll Inc. my two-week notice. Simple as that, my days are so f'n numbered!

"I was online Sunday looking up information on the east end and a few stats regarding wealth in Vancouver. They blew my mind," I prattled on, getting set to read aloud the numbers from a pink sticky-note. "It's crazy, man. Listen to this stat: percentage of population in lower income households. Commercial Drive area: thirty-seven percent. Kits and Kerrisdale: nineteen and sixteen percent. The Vancouver average: twenty-seven percent and get this: the percentage of population in lower income households in East Hastings is *seventy-nine percent!*" I crowed, Crusade of One in full swing.

"From what I hear, that number will go up when you move there. The problem is…"

But there was no stopping me. "No, no, no, no wait. Get a load of this. A Vancouver tourism website's charming description of our downtown east: 'From rough-and-tumble Hastings Street, where timeworn brickwork still exudes a wild, beer-for-a-dime, seaport town atmosphere.'"

"That is bang on. I do feel like a sailor when I'm stepping over crackheads at Main and Hastings."

"It's a mess," I said. "Hey, honk at this lunatic."

A monster truck (Roasted Chestnut 344-33) pulled into Dennis's lane, squarely cutting him off. Standard practice for Vancouver drivers, but I had a score to settle with the west. "Where do they get off?" I added. "These friggin' people buy these friggin' luxury cars and drive around like maniacs."

"Dude, that was a Toyota Camry, the most basic car on the road," Dennis said. "You need to chill. I'm putting you on a pot regimen, no questions asked."

"Still, everybody should be driving the same car. Have the government make one and dole them out."

"They'd likely choose the Camry for its handling and gas mileage. Hey, forget that guy. Can I ask what I did to deserve you?" Dennis said, looking poised to embrace, maybe even kiss me. "The Compassion Club has the best bud in the province, and since BC has the best in Canada and Canada the best bud in the world, the Compassion Club has the best bud in the world," he carried on. "I hear they have an actual store, like a market, where members go to shop. The different strains are posted on a chalkboard called The Daily Menu, varietals like Peruvian Slacker, Green Gooch, Story Time…"

"How do you know all this?"

"I know a guy who—"

"Of course you do."

"Too bad about this trip, can't wait to smoke a jibber with this Layne dude. Guy sounds super sketchy." Dennis was leaving the next day for Holland and Poland to meet with Briscoll's chief European distributors and would not arrive back until the middle of the following month.

"What's the Ultimate Team going to do without you?" I asked.

"Win, likely. I know I suck, but at least I'm aggressive out there. It's still a sport for Christ's sake. Two winners from my team bring their guitars to the field and they have a sing-a-long after every match," Dennis mourned, shaking his head distantly.

He rolled his truck to a stop in front of what was to be my place for only two more weeks.

"Pace yourself in Amsterdam," I said.

"Pace? What is this word 'pace'?"

On the Holland leg of his trip, Dennis would be manning a Briscoll Inc. tradeshow booth by day and judging the 14th annual Cannabis Cup by night. "Good luck with the pilgrimage east. See you in a month," he said, leaning over to give me a hearty side-arm hug.

I watched his rusty truck grumble down to the stop sign at the end of my block. His taillights winked at me as he turned out of sight.

Dennis's outfit (hideous though it was) and the Vancouver warm front inspired me to try for a jog around the neighbourhood. I had gone a significant stretch without exercise and could feel a real-time internal clogging.

I struggled from my screen door on. After clocking three city blocks my heavy breathing had regressed to a burning wisp. Eventually my cardiovascular system and my ego settled on run-a-block-walk-a-block.

Kitschylano residents were out in swarms, attacking the mild weather. My odious stance on west-enders had by then gone AWOL from rationale. Transfixed I stared at them all—the runners in their aerodynamic tights, the cyclists on their expensive road bikes, the walkers linked to their purebred pups—with evenhanded malice. Spitting venom under my wheezing breath I itemized them: *wealth-mongers, self-righteous spume, spiritual savages.* Here at the dawn of my Crusade of One, my socialist tour de force, I morphed into a regional racist, and the chafing on my inner thighs rounded out my overall disposition.

Sunset along the banks of Kitschylano was squandered on me that evening; sky afire with pink and red tufts of cloud, water still, violet, smooth as polished beach glass, wavy sand a milky tea brown. Giant beach logs rested on the surface like cinnamon sticks, there was a salty coastal breeze, and the jagged mountain ranges were turning a soft peach from meandering sun. A gentler version of the dogged midday fireball, the sun hung above the water holding on for us, trying to extend the day, allowing us time to redeem ourselves from another one wasted, from things unsaid. For Layne. Finally its perfect sphere was disrupted and swallowed by horizon; it melted into the water, taking our chance for atonement, possibly our last, down with it into the deep.

LAYNE APPEARED RELAXED WHEN HE ANSWERED THE door. He wore another long-sleeve shirt and shorts number, but this time layered it with a ratty purple housecoat, thin from wear. His shirt read **Stampeder Local 8341** and had a horse logo on the front. He later told me it was "just a T-shirt".

Two days before month end and Layne conveniently allowed me to move my paltry effects in early. There were also the small matters of delivering the trim paint, the rent, the damage deposit, and something pressing I needed to ask Layne in person.

Even with me at the bottom carrying the bulk of the weight, Layne provided little help with my dresser, struggling to support his end and noticeably winded from the effort. How does this guy handle landscaping? I was thinking when Layne asked about the paint: "No tricks? Stir and brush?"

"Stir it well. That's professional-grade coating; can't buy that in a paint store."

"Nathan Mills, Bachelor of Commerce," Layne read aloud. Out of habit I had taped one of my cards to the lid of one of the two pails. I was reminded of the slimy painter who used it as a toothpick upon receiving it from me. Layne pocketed it.

"As a business school grad, you'll appreciate the rental agreement I've written up for us."

Layne toured me over to the dining table outside of the kitchen, his shorts peeking out the bottom rung of thin purple cotton. On the table sat a pad of lined paper.

TENNANCY AGREEMENT FOR 1800 GRANDVIEW HIGHWAY N., UNIT 212
TENNANTS LAYNE RHODES AND NATE MILLS
AGREE TO THE FOLLOWING:

1. **Layne cooks.**
2. **Layne does all housework, including Nate's bathroom. No matter how dirty.**
3. **The place will be quiet and peeceful during the workweek.**
4. **Over-the-night guests need to be cheked with other.**
5. **$250 damage deposit to Layne for Mr. Chin.**
6. **Rent is $500 a month each.**
7. **If Nate stays out late, he will be quiet not to wakeup Mrs. Holme and Layne who will be sleeping.**
8. **Layne promises to smoke outside on the balconie, pot and cigs.**
9. **Layne loans Nate his leather jacket that is too small for him and his stereo that he doesn't use.**
10. **All decisions equal.**
11. **Anything not here solved by Vancouver Tennancy Act.**

Date: April 1, 2001

_____

Layne Rhodes

_____

Nate Mills

I tried not to find the contrast between Layne's verbal and

grammatical skills too startling.

"Please don't take this the wrong way," Layne beseeched me with hands pressed together as if in prayer. "There were those issues with the Kiwis and well, it's just a good idea to get it all down on paper," he continued. "It's nothing serious, but it is a legally binding contract. You should read it carefully before signing. I left room near the bottom if you wanted to add anything. Take it home if you need to. There's a copy for each of us to keep on file."

"No, I'll sign," I agreed. Too far gone in my quest not to let it slide, I excused the treaty as an endearing idiosyncrasy and nothing more. I signed both copies, confident that no judge would force me to wear Layne's leather jacket.

"I've inherited a jacket and a radio?" I inquired.

Layne had stashed both in my bedroom closet in anticipation of my arrival. Proud of the jacket, Layne insisted I try it on. I reluctantly agreed. The outer material was fractured by wear into a tatty, shattered-glass look. It hugged my midsection with a thick elastic waistband, and flopped over itself like a muffin top. For added flair at the front its designer had decided on a V-shaped course of tassels from shoulder to navel to shoulder.

The radio rested on the floor of my closet. "Rested" a choice word considering the age of the receiver and its bulk. In its heyday, this hi-fi had been sutured to a turntable or an eight-track cassette player—a find for an antique hunter had it not been devalued by makeshift masking tape knobs.

"Works like a dream," boasted Layne, his face beaming.

Since the dawn of my odyssey east, each and every alteration of time and space took on deeper symbolic meaning. Face value was no longer valid. My move represented a profound personal revelation, the building represented a lesson in prejudices, and now this wacky coat and clunky radio were embodying the importance of sharing. I gratefully accepted Layne's gifts without a fibre of good intention towards either one.

The light air of charity was ideal for broaching item four on our tenancy contract. A dear lifelong friend of mine, John Kopic (always known as Kope), had come into corporate VIP tickets for the Molson Indy Vancouver and was driving in that weekend—my first two nights with Layne—for a long overdue reunion. Two weeks prior I'd been telling Layne that I was, like himself, the dictionary's 'homebody' and wouldn't be surprised if I lived the term of the lease without, in his contractual language, an 'over-the-night guest'. And now I was losing face by giving him the lowdown on a visitor arriving within hours of my moving in, with designs to stay for a two-night stint. It was I who felt like a con man.

Layne stood patient through my penitent mumbling. "Sounds like fun. I'll cook," he bubbled, much to my relief.

What a nice guy, and how lucky am I. Eat that Nic, I thought to myself.

THE MORNING OF THAT TITANIC MOVING SATURDAY, Nic and I awoke side by side for the final time. There was only the matter of showers to make it official. When Nic returned from hers, dripping wetness from her head down, I had traded my towel for jeans. She gave me a gamesome wink and sashayed across the plush carpet to her suitcase in the far corner of the room. Bending at the waist with ease and purpose, she unzipped the bag slowly, her short towel nearly selling her out. The mango body scrub she loofahed over every inch of satiny skin played in the air.

My hetero mind jumped to the prospect of move-out sex. No strings attached; they had already been scissored. Nic turned my way and creased a loaded smile, allowing me full visuals of her near-naked body. Drier curls of blonde had fallen to her face unchecked. I walked around to the end of the bed; eyes ravaging her the entire way.

"Turn around," she said, playfully waving me in a circle with a pink undergarment. I smiled wryly and turned away. Of all the twists of fate!

"No peeking," she sang.

"I won't." I matched her childlike tone, playing the game, hungering to go where it was leading.

"*Oh. Ooooh. Mmmmm,*" Nic sighed. Bogus muscle aches to implant a vision in my head of her towel slipping off and her body stretching to contortion. Aroused to bursting, I imagined how it would come about: her bare arms slithering underneath mine and clasping at my chest, me turning to see a starved look in her tawny eyes, her naked body shivering with readiness. Or a nudge from behind flopping us onto the mattress, Nic rolling over to pounce on me animalistic. She'd treat the moment with the abandon and raunch it deserved, exercising the love-loss required for it to happen at all.

I raised my left foot behind me to indicate my desire to look back.

"Not ye-et," she chimed. "One more second…and…rea-dy."

Nic had stuffed her hour-glass elements into a tiny set of bra and panties (Cotton Candy 954-44), her dampened claret nipples peeking through lace soft as pillow talk. Then as I watched she buried everything under designer jeans, an angora sweater (Arctic Wolf 980-00), and a denim jacket. Folding her clammy towel she coolly lifted her eyes to catch the disappointment on my face.

"Sporting some severe morning wood there homeboy," Nic snickered. "Fuck man. Want me to leave you alone so you can milk that thing?"

I mounted the seat of my squawky mountain bike—a trashy ride stippled with rust—and peddled an eastern course. A silly smile beamed from my face for the birth of my liberation, and for the warm spell it had happened in. Taking time to enjoy the neither-here-nor-there limbo between lives, I zigzagged carefree through a simmering downtown Vancouver.

Sidewalk patios were plugged with the early lunch crowd. Murmurs of blended conversation and clattering cutlery on plates projected out to the street. The multitude of urbanites out in force, thousands upon thousands of individual angles and experiences, relit a sense of my insignificance. I envied this pre-noon set, wanting to take part in the socially grey, drinks-before-twelve, Caesars-to-start, weekend regimen. *You'll get yours soon enough. Kope is on the way*, I soothed myself.

Friends since kindergarten, Kope and I had a special bond. It started out superficially, as friendships between tots do—he had an extra Fruit Roll-Up and I let him borrow my Laurentian pencil crayons. Implausible as it was for two boys with so little in common, our friendship acquired a rudder made for deeper waters.

Kope grew up on a farm outside of St. Thomas. His address was Rural Route #2, which as a kid I found head-scratchingly bizarre. His parents were both first generation Croatian Canadians. Life on a farm, and a villainous older brother, had molded Kope into a tough burly kid.

His father Jakov, a barrel-chested immensity, prohibited television in the home. So Kope found other ways to entertain himself, like shooting baskets on a rim he nailed to the side of the barn, throwing baseballs into a peach basket strike-zone, playing keep-up with the soccer ball, stalking farm pests with pellet guns, and bettering push-up and chin-up records. By contrast I was raised inside of St. Thomas city limits on a street with a proper name, in a house with proper cable installation. My two chores were drying the dishes on Wednesday nights and cutting a lawn one-twentieth the size of Kope's. I was the archetypal television and video game catatonic.

Kope was the tallest kid his age in the county and for the two ages ahead of him. I was the shortest kid my age and the two ages below me. One thing we had in common: from the day we met in kindergarten to the end of elementary, we were the only two students to occupy the same spot in every class picture. Him, back row middle, and me, front row far right. Kope's mother used to gush over my babyish features, a maternal crush that hastily abandoned a lineage of beastly men.

We also shared a kinship with sports, though no common ground. Kope was the star athlete; big, strong, quick and determined. He excelled at any sport he gave his time to and even those he didn't. (Later Kope started at Linebacker for his university football team—a walk-on who had never played an organized game of football in his life). I entirely sucked at everything athletic.

But Kope didn't stop there. Granted academic scholarships and prizes his entire scholastic career, Kope posted the top male grade nearly every term. His tutoring in math and science, and in more time-sensitive situations, his willingness to be plagiarized, levied my B-average from year to year. In mathematics, antipodal points are points on the surface of a sphere which are diametrically opposite one another—so situated that a line drawn from one to the other passes through the centre of the sphere and forms a true diameter. In certain friendships, the only commonality is the friendship itself, the diametric line connecting the two, and that proves enough. This was me and Kope.

As the smallest kid each year I was an easy target for bullies. Unasked, Kope protected me from an unconscionable tally of beatings, but he went about it in a way that preserved my frail small-man ego. Segue to a damp day in grade five and a taste of what my schooling would have been like without my bodyguard. The afternoon recess bell had sounded, and the grade five boys ran out to the soccer field for a match. All but Kope, who was serving detention for gum chewing and as punishment, was forced to watch from the classroom window.

Without Kope there to captain team number one, I was duly picked last by his stand-in. It had rained over the lunch hour and the pitch had transformed into a bog of water and mud. One of the kids tagged the sport Muckball. The conditions slowed the game considerably and yet I still faltered its more sluggish pace. Two better-known Grade Seven bullies noticed the Twerp without his muscle around, so they decided it would be fun to pin him down in the turned-up soil and steal his shoes. I stood up after my unhanding, my socks squishing in the soft mud, coat and jeans soaked through, to chase after my footwear; lunging and falling in the slop to the amusement of a grandstand of grade five girls. Kope stood at the classroom window, watching my undoing with clenched teeth and white knuckles.

Mercifully the bell signaled the end of recess. Our teacher that year took a hard stance on tardiness, handing out detentions for every minute late to class, and so the bell incited a hairy stampede indoors. As a final nod to me each tough wound up his throwing arm and with the steady-handed artistic indifference of a bully, hucked my shoes as far as they could in opposite directions before joining the scramble inside.

Too dejected to rush I started out for my left shoe with shoulders slouched, tears collecting in the hollows of my eyelids and biting wind chilling my tiny wet frame. I swore and cried as I lifted the first shoe from the glop, despair increasing with my mental tally of lateness detentions. By the time I reached the vicinity of my right shoe, my crying and slobbering had reached its peak. My leaden socks flopped at my toes while I surveyed the landing area of the second shoe's touchdown. I was reeling. "I'm so-so-so path-pathetic. I wan-I wanna die!" I moaned, slamming my left shoe onto the ground. I sat in the mud and peeled my socks from my white feet. I was having a ten-year old's nervous breakdown.

Kope had been watching heavy-hearted at the window, wiping his hot breath from the glass as the kids ploughed in for class. The teacher instructed him to take his seat.

"He's leaving," Kope mumbled instead, and bolted from the classroom.

Out on the churned field he located two little shoes and high-stepped his way to me. I didn't look back when Kope implored me to stop, not wanting him to see my tears.

"Hey man. Where the frig are you going?" He walked as I jogged; his long strides counterbalancing my pace. "You'll get in trouble."

"Get away from me Kope. I'm not going back," I insisted, trying to block the adrenaline from unsteadying my voice.

Kope put a hand on my arm.

"LEAVE ME ALONE!" I wailed, yanking my arm back.

He knew I was not going back of my own free will, but he also knew the trouble I'd be in if I left. This was a strappable offense at an elementary school in the eighties. Kope knew better than to drag me back, though. The shame of being fireman-carried like a damsel in distress was no better than a hundred whippings.

"At least take your shoes." Knowing I did not want to face him, he tossed my muddied velcroes onto a patch of sidewalk ahead of me. I had stubbed my big toe twice on the uneven surface and my arches ached from the cold concrete, so the shoes came as a welcome relief. I stopped and put them on.

"I'll cover for you," Kope promised, and jogged back to class while I walked home in a huff, crying the entire way.

The following school day was another wet one, but Muckball had a teacher-enforced ban on it due to the damage to the soccer field. Instead we grade five boys met at our hangout underneath the tube slides. It wasn't long before the interrogation hit its full stride, and I was being prodded by the fellas.

"Did you really walk home?"

"Are you scared Mr. D'Arcangelo will give you the strap?"

"I heard you were crying your eyes out, huh Sally?"

They laughed in unison, all but Kope. Boy Bawling made for a juicy headline in grade five, an age when it was no longer socially acceptable even to have a bit of a pout.

"Crying? All I saw was a fist," Kope piped in, rubbing his bicep with a wincing look, silencing the laughter.

"He hit you?" one of the boys asked. The second question "And it hurt you?" was implied.

"He friggin' decked me when I gave him his shoes. Where was his backup on the field, by the way?" Kope looked set to hand out a round of his patented Charlie Horses. The group shimmied uncomfortably in their woodchip seats. "My friggin' arm still hurts."

In an instant, my epic meltdown had dissolved into playground legend.

The bell screamed shortly thereafter, and we ran for it. In the cloakroom two of my classmates stopped to congratulate me: "Nice job man," one said. Then the other: "You must have really *smoked* him."

To thank him I confronted Kope about his story at lunch. He played dumb, sticking by his word even with only me there. "Frig, you don't remember? You nailed me, I swear." Kope could be very convincing and the edginess of the situation did make my recollection somewhat spotty. After a few more reinforcing comments about his sore arm, and seeing the black and blue round (it turned out he'd bruised himself at home with a clothespin), I was so swayed that I actually apologized for hurting him.

Kope's emotional awareness was as precocious as his girth. He was the Bobby Fisher of feeling and he was my friend.

At the time of his planned visit, Kope worked as a city manager for Chrysler Canada, an exalted position for his age and a testimony to his hard work and dedication. He boasted a six-figure salary, subordinates twenty years his senior, and could have his pick of New Releases, fuelled and fresh off the lot, for his road trip west from Calgary.

My parents frequently asked me about Kope's whereabouts and his up-to-the-minute accolades. They knew his state of affairs well—a *St. Thomasonian* didn't toot without the whole town knowing whether three provinces or a world away. Their asking was a subconscious attempt to get me thinking about my own direction; they hoped Kope's conquests would spark in me the impetus to accomplish grand feats of my own. But Kope was a dominant, unflappable force with the complete package: brains, work ethic, looks, physique, reckless abandon, and charisma. The type profoundly aware of their surroundings, to the point where it seems the universe comes at them in clear slow motion, to the steady rhythm of a metronome. What was more he was a pure gentleman; always knowing the right things to say and rarer still, meaning them. His was a soul you could eat off of. Best of all, below the commercially viable traits and overage of talent, he remained that caring ten year-old. Kope, my dynamo of a best buddy. The one I loved to, hated to, love.

Skirting the city bustle, I cycled onto Commercial Drive. There the traffic was as profuse as in the downtown but less hurried, which I attributed to courtesy and a rounded sense of community. It came as a drastic change and welcomed relief from the egocentric hustle of Kitschylano.

Midway down the strip a mob had gathered around a simple wooden stage built next to a war memorial cenotaph in a shaded parkette. The people on hand were plopped on the grass enjoying an open-air performance, a one person play with one prop—an old-fashioned burgundy suitcase. Through the player's deft acting and grasp of mime, the audience was led through a range of characters and scenes. Swiftness and sound effects transformed his single piece of luggage into a train car, a coffin, a park bench, an accordion, a phone booth, hung laundry, and more. An uplifting sight, this marvel of human potential. I watched the production from the curb, and even flinched when he let slip his imaginary tray of glasses.

My thoughts rebounded back to Kope. He had lived in Calgary for nearly a year and this would be his first visit to the west coast. Calgary leaned conservative—I gathered from Canadian impressionism—whereas Vancouver was more avant-garde (despite the frequency of moustaches), more sketchy, but in a good way. Kope would be taken aback by the condition of my building and surrounding blocks. Layne would undoubtedly weird him out at first. But over the course of the next two days, he'd see past the outer layer and revolutionize his perceptions as I had. I itched for the opportunity to be his cultural trainer. Things were coming full circle from our youth and it was now my turn to look out for Kope, to fireman-carry *him* to a holistic insight on life. Reverse the current.

Starry-eyed, I found myself pedalling away from the performance without the conscious decision to do so.

When I wheeled up to my Grandview flat, there were again no signs of life outside the place. The only changes were the position of the hot sun overhead and the clothes on my back, until I was startled by a familiar figure. I could see him not ten feet away through an open door to the unit opposite the crook in the L. Lower units on that side were unconventionally designed bachelors with bomb shelter square footage and sliding glass entrances; in this one the shades had been drawn back, lighting a man on a made bed. The man was Mark. I knew straight away from his clothing and tattoos.

I walked my bike closer to the door, refocusing to the change of light and shadow. Most of Mark was horizontal, his two feet flat on the carpet (Earth Worm 666-96), knees bent at right angles with the end of the bed. His eyes were wide open, staring at the ceiling blankly. As if he had somehow refocused through the plaster and wood, through the overhead apartment, onto the shapes of the irregular clouds drifting above.

"Hey Mark," I called, my uplifted spirits bumping the volume of my voice. Mark paid me no attention. I scanned for vitals from the doorway. His chest bobbed to narrowly timed beats. He was alive. Freaky to watch someone sleep with their eyes open. And how can anyone sleep with their legs cranked like that? I pondered and let him be.

Layne was out someplace. Left to my merriness, I carried forward my idea to surprise him with a big grocery shop: a Day One gesture of stupendous goodwill. I checked the fridge and cupboards for inventory and was put back by the barrenness. I made off for provisions, certain of two things: one, I would not double up on anything; and two, Layne would be charmed. He had earlier confirmed that the Safeway at Broadway and Commercial was our only local grocer, so I primed myself for the humbling tableau of poverty-struck people and left on foot, fearing my ride would be stolen from the store bike rack.

Near Commercial Drive I choked on a rotten stench that rode the tunneled breezeway of the back alley servicing businesses on the main drag. In back of a corner store, halos of maggoty decomposing trash were piled around two overflowing dumpsters. I breathed through my mouth until I'd turned onto Commercial and out of stink's range. Now under the SkyTrain overpass and over the train track underpass, I was at the notorious type of place on Vancouver's East Side where the homeless and drug-addled roosted in numbers. I didn't dare look at anyone. Instead I eyed the cracks in the sidewalk, signs on the buildings, the stoplight's red hand then the white walking man, and rediscovered I was a bit of a scaredy-cat.

The Safeway proved a large, clean, fluorescent-lit facility boasting deli, bakery, pharmacy, florist and wine shop. The patrons were not the streetlife outside, but visibly self-sustaining people. It hit me that those hurting outside could not afford this food or the means to cook it, relying on food banks or dumpster-diving for their meals. I annexed a push cart, riding its momentum away from the guilt and into the produce section.

Having a chef at home required a new approach to food selection. I needed to think raw ingredients and seasonings. I needed to evolve my scurvy-seducing diet of soup, sandwiches and cereal. Shocked by my ignorance of cuisine, I butchered product names as I passed: bocconcini, pecorino, rapini, kale, millet, quinoa, tahini, cumin, tarragon, polenta, occasionally dropping items that looked meal-malleable into the steel cage.

In line at the deli counter, I watched three white coats at work against a backdrop of white tiles. Two of the butchers chopped and shaved different cuts on a stainless steel countertop as the other fed portions to a grinder. Bloody red chunks of fibrous meat went in, pink squibbish strands of pulverization piled out. The tiny speckles of white fat in the coils were the only remnants of the flesh's original form.

When the final item had been loaded onto the belt and scanned by their laser, I had purchased $175.00 worth of food, $100 of which I had never processed in my life. I exited with so many shopping bags in each hand that the outer ones were practically horizontal, bunching like the white curd on cauliflower. My only inheritance from my father's imposing frame is his broad shoulders. From the neck down I look like a field mushroom, but my shoulders do make effective braces for grocery bags.

The bags slowed my progress considerably. There was time to connect with the situation, to peer into the exhausted faces without damming any rush of emotion. Handcuffed to my shopping, I felt exposed, vulnerable, and sick for them. It was a start.

The westerly sun cast my shadow on pained faces hunched against a brick building, black reflections of my grocery bundles swiping directly under their noses. If I hadn't felt like a schmuck before, I was now hauling a ludicrous load of food past one of the hungriest corners in Canada.

But I'd overestimated my inheritance, I had gained not even a block before the muscles in my neck and shoulders, stretched like cocked slingshots, ached unbearably. I set the bags down near the guardrail of the overpass to loosen my gawky upper half, letting blood flow to my purpling fingertips while I admired a passing train. From here the Canadian National Railway entrenchment provided sightlines to the downtown and the mountain ranges cascading beyond. The white roof of BC Place stadium beamed in sunshine, its pearly dome anchoring the city skyline. The long train rattled out from under my feet snaking the tracks towards the container-swamped shipping docks of the Burrard Inlet. There immaculate cruise liners and sea-sullied cargo ships dodged each other's headings.

That quagmire of train tracks and switchbacks, how do they keep everything straight? I thought insincerely, comfortable in not knowing. Then I glowered west, in the general vicinity of Kitschylano. Flanked by ocean and superfluity, spared the sights and sounds of calamity and hardship, out of sight of this train dug deep in its trench struggling to push on, out of earshot of its long steel axles churning over wheels and its whistle screaming with rising pressure. Kitschylano the scourge!

"This is community grub. Please, help yourself to anything," I declared with elaborate fake modesty. *Cook to your heart's desire*, my wits were really saying.

"Real nice of you Nate. I was planning a shop."

My clunky cell phone rang, stalling the idle chat.

"I think I'm here?" Kope said, likely hoping he had the wrong place.

"You're early. I'll be down."

Kope had arrived in a 300M (Jet Stream 110-10), Chrysler's newest model. We hugged, stiff and manly. My St. Thomas friends all greet one another with these cold homophobic embraces, starching their backs to make sure that their chests and their pelvises are separate. Funny, here we are, two grown men, best friends since primary, willing to take a bullet for each other—taking special care to avoid chiming our nipples together. Squeezes from Dennis Zimmer and his gang were warmer, freer.

"That's a pretty crazy spot back there," Kope commented in his padded, considerate manner, thumbing towards the huddled masses at Broadway and Commercial.

"Yep, always a party," I answered.

Viewing the decrepitude of 1800 Grandview Highway North rendered Kope speechless, but he held true to his famous poker-faced savoir fare. He looked tired—a thick five o'clock shadow and looping black sags under his chestnut eyes—but he had a talent for outrunning exhaustion; keeping his demeanour in check and never bellyaching about fatigue.

Layne treated Kope to a royal welcome: taking his suitcase, intoning his 'sincere pleasure', and offering to 'whip up' a snack if he was hungry from the long journey.

"Pleased to meet you too Layne. Thank you, but I'm fine," Kope returned crisply. I wanted to save my tired friend from Layne's fanatical onslaught. I suggested he drop his bags in my room.

"What a drive," Kope said, flopping on my futon.

"Did it in one shot? You're a bit of a maniac."

"Gorgeous stretch, but I'll see most of the views on my way back. Forget all that, what happened with Nic? Last I heard you two were cool."

"I guess it's true what my Uncle Jerry says: If it flies, floats, or f-u-c-k-s, lease it."

"Your Uncle Jerry sounds like a gem."

"That's what they tell me."

Layne sensed the gaiety and rapped on my open door. "Nate mentioned you were a Calgary Man. I've never been, but I know someone living in Calgary."

I *know someone living in Calgary*. The statement hung in the room; the epitome of a child blabbing anything for the sake of being heard. Kope struggled to muster a fitting response, just as one does for the general proclamations: 'I like stuff' and 'Food is good'.

"Well Layne, it's a nice city," Kope managed politely.

"Sorry. You guys catch up." Layne went off as quickly as he came. The discomfort from his pop-in still hung in the air.

"That's alright," Kope said to his retreating footsteps.

True to form the coin flip of conversation landed on Kope's love life. He was known for legendary tales of conquests and was rolling one out when he rubbed his stubble and, drowsy, got sidetracked. "I forgot my razor. Remind me to stop when we get beer."

Layne shuffled along the polished hardwood from the living room couch to my doorway. He said, with a slight pant to his speech from the physical exertion, "I've got you covered my friend. There's an extra razor with fresh blades in my medicine cabinet. Yours when you need it buddy." Layne fired a six-shooter salute at Kope and retreated back to the left edge of the couch to eavesdrop for his next opening.

I frowned at Kope. A look to say *This behavior is new for him.*

"You ought to recharge before tonight. I can watch some TV. We'll do a quick sightsee and a late dinner."

The mention of dinner echoing down the corridor set Layne's peg legs in motion for a third time. His purple robe flapped in the current he created.

"Gentlemen, dinner is sorted. I have to insist." Layne then seconded his own motion: "John Kopic's first night in Van, so we'll give him a proper first meal. A base for that beer you boys plan on swillin'."

Layne waltzing us through courses of culinary delight did trump the fast food slam dance I had in mind. "Thanks," I said lightly, still jangled by his obsessiveness.

"Yes. Thank you Layne," Kope added more honestly, with a gleaming smile.

Glee radiated from Layne's face. He bobbed the two of us

a toadyish nod and strutted out to his smoking balcony for a triumphant joint. Since Kope's arrival he had been acting like an overexcited child on Christmas Eve. *Where was the charm?* I thought. *The reserved Layne? My endearing underdog?*

I left Kope to sleep. Surely he couldn't have missed the tired rusty bicycle, the old tabletop stereo with masking-tape tooling, and the dated set of golf clubs in my closet as he slipped into shorts, opting not to tell his hard-up friend about the new set of Taylor Made ™ sticks he won at the company golf tournament, the Alaskan cruise he earned for destroying productivity targets, or his big raise.

Plunked on the couch I wrung the neck of a bag of salty nacho chips, shoveled a clump of tomato salsa straight from the jar, and shattered the load in my teeth. Some of the bigger shards scratched my throat, which I remedied with an ice-cold can of Schweppes. *Crack! Phssssss.* The carbonation soothed the scored walls of my throat and the scent of ginger tickled my nose. Layne passed me on the way inside from his smoke. "Watch the spills bud," he instructed, smelling of doobie. To his bedroom door he went, shutting and, in defiance of his stated intent to promote a social atmosphere in the apartment, locking himself inside. My curiosity piqued. What, or who, was Layne harbouring in that room? Was he a scientist with a secret paint lab? A terrorist? A pot smoking superhero?

I clicked away from those guesses with the power button on the futuristic Sony Vega remote. *Time to kill time. Australia, here I come,* I thought. But my festive mood was quickly spooked by the sound of television static. Black and white specks jostled for position on every channel. *Shhhhhhh-Click-Shhhhhhh-Click-Shhhhhhh!*

I knocked on Layne's door in search of instruction.

"No cable," Layne said matter-of-factly from behind his door. A strategic oversight from our interview. My regard for him was receding. Who owns a television of this quality and doesn't spring for cable? I frowned a deeply furrowed frown.

Properly bored I sat on the couch visualizing Layne's leafy plants—my ticket to Australia and a life without paint. The shrubs' life cycle, from sprout to harvest, fast-framed through my imagination like a David Suzuki eco special. Selling weed had initially struck me as sordid and seamy, but I was amending that stance and so was Canada at the time. Jean Chretien had made strides towards decriminalization by pushing for lighter sentences for the possession of small amounts of marijuana. If pot were legalized, I read in the *Sun*, it would top every industry as British Columbia's largest legitimate source of revenue. Everybody smoked. Four of the five department heads at Briscoll Inc. had smoked rap video blunts outside my work Christmas party for Pete's sake.

Heck, I had the Prime Minister and half the west coast on my side. There was enough cushioning in the facts to allow me to sell a little weed *and* sleep at night.

THE TORONTO MAPLE LEAFS BEACH TOWEL I'D GIVEN Kope wrapped my waist one-and-one-half times; Kope's broad beaded frame shrunk it to the size of a tea towel. I briefed him on our plans, tilting my head to give him privacy as he muscled his clothes over wet spots.

I felt jumpy and raring to go, shifting on the balls of my feet in anticipation of popping Kope's eyes with local culture. "You shaved?" I asked redundantly, pointing at his fresh face.

"Layne left me a razor in the bathroom. Nice guy."

At that point Layne began thunder-stomping the hardwood to my room. *Wham! Wham! Wham! Wham!* Kope and I froze in place. Layne appeared in the doorframe, red-faced, his veins bulging, furious, Layne shouted: **WHO LEFT THAT FUCKING BATHROOM LIGHT ON? WHO THE FUCK WAS IT?**

HE STOOD THERE SEETHING, FACE PURPLER THAN stewed beets. Keeping wild eyes fastened on us he raised the back of one hand to wipe spittle from his bottom lip as if acting out a one-man play of his own. I was lost for words, stomach and neck stiff as a potted tree. I had no point of reference, no previous learning experience to draw on. I couldn't say to myself: *Remember the last time you moved in with a raging psychopath. You told him, "Re-lax", at which point he stabbed you in the neck with a pair of marijuana pruners and fed you to his rusty juicer. You are not saying that again.*

So in his honourable way, Kope jumped on the grenade and absorbed the blow for friend and countryman. "I had a shower," Kope said steadfastly. "All on me."

Layne calmed his breathing and the colour in his face lightened. "Nate and I are trying to build a respectful fellowship. We both pay the bills, so I ask you to keep that under consideration during your stay."

"I will Layne, my apologies."

Don't apologize to him! I wanted to say.

"Already water under the bridge my friend. Be back for seven, fellas, pork chops are on the menu," Layne said. Like the freakish touchdown of a funnel cloud, it was over.

We held our tongues until we were out of the apartment. "That was odd," Kope said in the car, tactfully reserved.

But Kope's light comment goaded an uncontrollable heaving of emotion. As we cruised north on Commercial into the heart of The Drive, I began unrolling what I knew of Layne so far: cancer, weed, the Compassion Club, cooking, cleaning, the Sony, the tenancy agreement, Mark, Mrs. Holme. Then I told him about me: the painters, Australia, Dennis's wisdom, the Toyota Camry, Nic, Kitschylano, Layne, local wealth statistics, my Crusade of One. I unwound to the core.

"I don't know. Maybe he deserves a bit of leeway," I finished, "or maybe he is certifiably insane."

Though he prided himself on staying a meat-and-potatoes man, Kope had dined in many of Canada's top-tier restaurants during his rich term with Chrysler. "Maybe it's a chef thing. They can be touchy bastards when it comes down to the finer details. You know, plating the marrow drizzle at three o'clock and the sprig of dill at nine o'clock. Nitpicky, proper—what's the word?"

"Meticulous?"

"That's it."

"Why Mr. Kopic, I was unaware of your culinary repartee," I teased.

"Well, up until a second ago, I was unaware of your drug cartel."

We laughed. Kope set my mind at ease, with so much invested in my roommate, I found it easier to excuse Layne.

Sights set on the Cypress Mountain lookout on the north shore, I directed Kope to the Second Narrows Bridge, one of two linking the city central to the hillside communities of North and West Vancouver. He punched the gas and his 300M gracefully accelerated without chugs or engine din, the only working sound a muffled buzz, like a swarm of happy bees.

As we crossed over the bridge Nature's local wonders came alive in the soft orange of waning sun and the emerald green of fir trees gulping cars into their raven shadows. Cobalt currents of the Burrard Inlet washed the brown pack shoreline below, and at water's edge, two gargantuan mounds of yellow sulphur powder, standing solitary, glowed like a landmark from another planet.

Kope tutored me on his car's features, gibbering about cylinders, horsepower, hemi-engines and rear-alloy suspension. I don't speak Car, so I nodded frequently and timed my oohs and ahs to the tide of his facial expressions and pregnant pauses. The highway bent west and widened to six ascending, tree-hugged lanes. "This is what I'm talking about!" Kope shouted, punching the gas and quickly posting fifty clicks over the legal limit. Scared witless I alerted Kope to the latest crackdowns on speeding and the steep increases in fines due to a rash of street racing deaths, including one involving a policeman in Richmond. But Kope knew only one gear. He paid my warning no mind as he gained altitude, blazing past cars so fast we made them look stationary, flashes of Vancouver Centre in the tree gaps to our left and huddled trees climbing the steep, unforgiving mountain to our right. We passed the Capilano exit in a blink. To calm myself I told Kope about Vancouver's miracle baby. Earlier that same year a woman had dropped her eighteen-month old baby girl over the railing of the Capilano Suspension Bridge. The infant plummeted seventy meters, rattling several tree branches before colliding with a rocky ledge below. Miraculously she not only survived the drop but suffered only minor cuts and bruises. The mother later told authorities her daughter had wriggled out of her grasp and over the handrail, but the RCMP became skeptical and the media had a field day once it was discovered that the baby had Down Syndrome. Speculation held that the mother had dropped the child to cut herself free. A confounding account of — what? Despair? Kope reduced it to being effed up. I directed him to exit at Cypress and we took on the steep road leading to the lookout, its awe-inspiring panorama. He eased his racer into one of the wide stalls and I was relieved to be at rest.

"Wow!" Kope watched the cars below, crawling like tropical bugs across the Burrard Inlet and over the regal Lion's Gate Bridge. Tankers like tub toys cut white stripes out to the ocean; the vast trees of Stanley Park, bunched together like a giant turtle shell, seemed humbled by elevation. The entire throw of scenery looked like a model in a miniatures museum. The euphoria brought by this view would surely prove the perfect aperitif for Kope's first night in Van City.

After a long look we cruised at a safer speed back to Commercial Drive. Scenic rush had had a calming effect on Kope's driving as well. Since time was cooperating, I had Kope stop at Dan's Beer Supplies. The owner of Storm Brewery next door recognized me as Dennis's Friend, just as in high school I was Kope's Sidekick. Unsolicited he suited me with a sixer of Storm IPA in return for promising to tell Dennis to stop in when he arrived back from Europe. Though Dennis was the catalyst, I still felt connected, like a mobster receiving tribute from a shopkeeper. Kope smiled at me in the car afterwards, apparently impressed. Unwilling to spoil my own cheerful mood I refused to dwell on the contrast between a six-pack of beer and VIP passes to the Molson Indianapolis.

"Craft brew from an indie." I breasted Kope on the finer points of brewing as he took in Commercial's nighttime bustle.

When it neared seven o'clock on Kope's designer watch (linked to his stovepipe wrist by the last possible punch-hole) we headed back to Grandview Highway North to dine.

Part Three

Quick Tips for a Flawless Do-It-Yourself Painting Experience

Step 3:

Pour out some of your paint into a proper paint tray. This can be a messy step. Adequately protect yourself and your work area from ugly drips and spills.

THE FRONT DOOR OPENED A QUARTER WAYS AND jammed on seven pairs of treadless, time-worn shoes strewn on the downstairs landing. I tucked through without strain where Kope, red-faced, had to wriggle his might inside.

"Great, the boys are here," I overheard Layne say upstairs.

Whiffs of charred air polluted the normally sweet nose of the place. At the top of the stairs, we were greeted by Layne and a pack of ragtag houseguests squished around the dinner table behind him. Layne had inserted a wooden leaf and rounded up enough chairs to accommodate his company. "Boys, your timing is perfect. Please sit."

Kope sat as I followed Layne into the kitchen to refrigerate the Storm IPA and sneak a word.

"Picked up some brewskis I see," Layne said as I slotted bottles into the fridge door.

"What's the deal out there?" I said.

"Saturday Supper."

"Saturday Supper?" I shook my head.

"Oh man, I meant to tell you bud. On the weekends I invite our hungry neighbours in for a hot meal. It's all good." Layne flicked the oven off and left to entertain his party.

His arms-length charity efforts were impressive and

concerning. I had only ever played a part in seasonal, distanced martyrdom—dropping money in a Salvation Army kettle at Christmas, toting a Unicef box on Halloween, or donating non-perishables to the food bank at Thanksgiving. Weren't there inherent risks in turning your apartment into a soup kitchen for the desperate and confused? I was already faltering in the face of my new ideals. Martyrdom: easier said than done.

The two seats reserved for Kope and I were not side by side. Kope sat on the kitchen end of the table, pressed between Layne at the head and a smelly old man with decaying teeth. He wore sullied grey slacks and a white T-shirt that doubled as a handkerchief, with telling red, yellow and green sinus crust on the chest. His cheek and jowl sagged from the bone on one side in a Bell's Palsy laze. Long hairs curled from his oversized nose and ears and the retreating white hair on his head made tangled greasy lace. The man suffered from dementia and asked Kope the same three questions twice over. Kope politely engaged the stranger, smiling and responding each time he was asked his name, age and political affiliation.

The chair beside the old man is empty in my mind, its occupant a phantom of fleeting recollection. I try to visualize this missing person, reconstruct the face, but I blank. My seat faced Layne's, I was in the mommy chair. The other six eaters stared catatonically at their own plates as if looking down wells. To my left sat three Caucasian males. Two looked to be in their mid-to-late thirties and the other in his early teens—the hardest to take. This mere tot had long shags of chestnut hair poking out from under a Blue Jays baseball cap. He looked malnourished, a grey cotton shirt darkened by street grime and dirty three-quarter-length jeans hanging on him like they would on an unstuffed scarecrow. An oily gloss covered much of his freckled face, but his eyes were a clear sky blue. At a stretch, he could double for my brother.

Skipping Grace, the youth rapidly shoveled food into his mouth, barely chewing the loads.

"Tony!" Layne barked, pounding the table with his fist, sending his fork to the floor. The hungry youngster looked up startled. He hesitantly said "Tommy," through a mouthful of food.

"Tony, Tommy, whatever. Do you know how rude it is to start eating before everyone at the table gets their share? In some countries they'd lop your fucking arms off at the elbows!"

Tommy shied his eyes away from Layne and looked back down his well.

"And don't talk to me with your mouth full. It's fucking disgusting," Layne added.

Kope's dark brown eyes widened and fixed on me.

To my immediate right sat the lone female. A wide band of tattoos wrapped her wrist that rested beside my plate. By stealthy glimpses I made out its interlacing thorny green stems and red roses. Her pale arm through the ink tugged me back to poinsettia napkin rings my mother would resuscitate from the dusty attic for Christmas Dinner. Sunrays from the heat wave had left her with raccoon sunglasses striping on her face and chapped lips. She wore a pair of seasoned white sweatpants and matching sweatshirt too small for her meaty upper half and giving way to the siderolls of her stomach. From pilfered glances at her profile I saw her looks as plain, but when she pressed the back of my hand with her index finger as if she were ringing a doorbell and pivoted her head to introduce herself, she revealed an easy beauty: jet-black hair parted in the middle bordered metallic green eyes. There was a soft pudge to her face and she had a cute open-mouthed smile. "He mentioned you just moved in? It's Nate, right?" she began in a raspy voice. I nodded, feeling at my least social. "You will love Commercial. It has a spiritual energy. I'm Tonya, by the way, and this is my boyfriend Reggie." She pointed to the lanky blonde man wearing an army green T-shirt in the next seat. "Reggie, Nate." Reggie gave me a quick wink and went back to chowing. Tonya snickered over the exchange. Her throaty laugh eased the impression left by her tattoo.

From there, our conversations were continually stamped out by Layne's patrolling.

"Shawn! If you want more, ask for it to be passed. Don't reach your arms across the table like an idiot octopus."

"You! Don't wipe your face with your hands. Use your

napkin."

"Tonya! There is no need to drape your arms around your plate. Nobody's going to steal your dinner in here, so please get them off the table." Tonya slid her arms to her sides and looked at me with eyes crossed and tongue out, chummily nudging me.

Layne's indignity was appalling. He hailed down orders like a deranged den mother setting out to feed the hungry, seemed more like intent to sound off on them. Saturday Supper was entrapment; entrapment with low-grade bait: food that stared up at you. *You are a gullible fool,* it smugly said. There were three large dishes: instant mashed potatoes, Green Giant frozen vegetable medley (corn, pea, and carrot) and pork chops. The potatoes had a thin runny consistency and oozed about the plate. The vegetables were water-logged from neglectful boiling; biting into the niblets was like chewing teardrops. And the poor pig, cooked leathery tough, clanked the Corningware like air-hockey pucks. It was meat that could grip and uproot a tooth.

I held Layne in silent contempt while tasting courteous portions of each course. In the kitchen when I was fetching my fourth glass of meal lubrication from the tap, I overheard Layne stand up at the table and hush his silent onlookers—Saturday's chosen ones. "Friends, please," Layne said calmly, smiling under his moustache. *Here it is,* I thought. After a bad day turned into erratic spurts of bullying, Layne was going to steady his course with words of encouragement. Despite having lied about his chef's skills and leaving out his anger-management issues, an inspirational speech from Layne, rooted in his best intentions, would salvage our otherwise disastrous first day and gain us some footing after our initial backslide. After all, I didn't need cable TV or a live-in chef, just an even-tempered roommate. And maybe a pound of his weed to sell. *How will it go?* Layne will thank everyone for coming and for their patience with his obsession for table etiquette. He'll comment on the importance of sharing and of people coming together to denounce selfishness and celebrate the human spirit. *Right on Layne. I don't care about the fibbing. You were desperate. No hard feelings. Be that level, curious man I first met and we can forget about this demented dinner party. Please, I need this.*

Something has to catch!

I scurried to my seat.

"Feel free to keep eating. Life has put you people in harm's way. I pray for a shift that favours you all." Layne spread his arms out ecclesiastically, regaining the room for himself and redeeming himself for me. "Thank you for opening yourselves to my charity. Although I cannot sympathize with your situations, I can, and do, empathize."

With Layne standing over us in his purple vestment, arms raised and overrun by hair, the scene roughly depicted Leonardo da Vinci's Last Supper, an image from one of my cousin Angie's Art History textbooks.

"I hope you enjoyed the meal, but you are strangers in my home and that brings a level of responsibility." He continued, now cooling. "You see that coffee table in the living room behind you. Everybody look," he said, pointing past me towards the flower-patterned sofa. "I store my valuables in the middle drawer of that table. Right now there is a wad of cash and a zippy of weed in there. Stealing from me, especially after the generosity I've shown, would be a bold move indeed. If I see any of you so much as looking in the direction of that room"—Layne scanned the eyes of his disciples counter-clockwise, searching for his Judas. He served Kope and I the same accusing looks as the rest: all of us were suspect—"I will have no choice but to respond with force. Throw you down these stairs and into the streets where you came from. I'll be well inside the confines of the law to do so. So just test me. I dare ya." He had derailed again. Talking as though he had foiled a grand heist, the homeless people's master plan to steal the loot nobody knew he had. Threatening to beat up a table of emaciated street persons. I regretted sitting idle while letting Layne run amok, but what is a spineless boy to do?

A full-scale hiatus followed Layne's flare-up. I was touched when Tonya risked a look back in the direction of the coffee table to say goodbye to me, though he wouldn't have gotten a hand on her with Kope around. "Really nice to meet you Nate. See you on The Drive."

"You too Tonya."

"Here, a present." Tonya handed me a thick rubber band she had readied in the muff pocket of her sweatshirt. The strap was white with looping designs and an inspirational three-letter word was written neatly in block letters in the middle using glittery silver marker. "A bracelet. I make them out of scraps of rubber."

"No rubbers I hope…" I stopped short. The reply had sprung from my lips before my brain could distill it. Intended as a harmless joke, the blip instead cast a net of sickening insinuation. My jaw dropped as the blood rushed to my face.

Tonya pardoned the comment. "No rubbers. Ha, ha," she said with kindly fabricated laughter.

"I didn't mean…" I tailed off.

"Be good," Tonya said and smiled, letting me off the hook completely.

Layne bid adieu to those clustered on the stairwell with about-faced schizophreni. "Be safe, people. Godspeed."

When all had fled, he excused himself to Kope and I and walked toward the veranda for an after-dinner blaze.

"Are you sure it's safe to leave us alone with your not-so-secret stash?" I quipped, disdain trumping my fear and braver for having Kope at my side. Layne stopped beside the couch, dipped his chin to his chest, and turned to face me with a look of resignation. Discomfitted by the tension, I felt my eyes blinking rapidly. Kope feigned stacking plates, hanging on Layne's response.

Layne chose his words carefully. "Nate, Kope, I'm sorry. The warning was not intended for you." As he spoke, Layne rolled a cigarette between his thumb and two fingers, looking at it as though he had written his next sentence around the filter. "It's rewarding to make a small difference in their lives and I am grateful for the opportunity, but you must understand that people under hardship become, well, unpredictable." *They* are unpredictable? I chewed over the irony as he continued. "You must set ground rules. Make them aware of the swift repercussions in store for those willing to take advantage of your kindness. It's unpleasant, but necessary. Like death and…" *Celine Dion?* I thought at random. "…taxes."

"You told them where you hide your money," I said. My hand opened to the ceiling in a waitering, somewhat effeminate, gesture, as if I was balancing an invisible tray of wine glasses.

"Aha. That's the idea: lay it out for them. Solve the riddle. Show them the rainbow to the pot of gold, bud." He had shown them where to find his pot and his gold: Layne had me lost, and impatient. "I'm saying, for those of you casing the place, wondering where Grandpa Layne hides the cookie jar, he'll save you the trouble. But heed the warning friends: you take, you burn. They know you mean serious business if you are willing to show your stash. It becomes a powerful statement, like a dare." Then Layne shifted gears. "You gents want to join me for a little toke? This is Purple Pie Man. A Club staple." He held up a tubby two-paper joint plump with government sanctioned pot.

We declined.

"Suit yourselves. Toke dodging is allowed," he said before stepping out back.

"That's why I love living with Layne. He doesn't force his drugs on me," I told Kope, though I was freefalling on the inside.

Kope snuck past the grow room curtain, chilled bottle of Storm in hand, to explore the op for the first time. I started in on the dishes. I imagine the heat from the high-wattage bulb warming his face as he palmed one of the nine-pointed leaves and wondered what had led me down this road.

Dishes cleaned and put away, my last order of business was to jettison the bones in the garbage room. Too lazy to put on my size sevens I departed in Kope's boats—leather slip-on loafers large enough to wear over my shoes like my father's galoshes. "Garbage room is through the outer hallway, first door on your right," Layne had told me after I'd signed his screwy tenancy contract. How different my situation had looked only just the other day. The hallway started at the corner of the L between our own entranceway and Mark's and channeled under the building to a small open air courtyard, off which were the utility and trash rooms.

Evening's last light marked the courtyard at the end of the covered hallway and swathed a tall slim stranger approaching the dim arcade. He wore a thick coat, much too padded for the inclement heat, and walked in a laboured hunch with arms crossed tightly at his chest, as though gripping the fading memory of a fallen friend. I met his eyes the second before he was engulfed by dimness. Scuttling along, ridiculous in Kope's clown shoes, I'd expected my sheepish blush to be met with a smirk of amusement. But his grey skin hugged the bone of his face so tight his eyeballs bulged; his pupils were wide and his dilated stare gave back a blankness of emotion only found in the pages of an entomologist's reference book.

I starched my back and drew away.

But the man made way for another morose figure beyond him in the open air of the quad. At the far side of an elevated flower garden overrun by spiky weeds, this figure was bent at the haunches like a kangaroo. Suddenly he sprang back rapidly, rapping his back off the wall behind him. With force enough to knock a person's wind out he now continuously slammed himself backwards against the brick, pitching forward from the shock, flinging backwards again, over and over. I wished I had a pillow in my hands to run and cushion the blows, though I doubted I'd dare go close enough to prop it into place. The slammer's face was hidden by an oversized hoodie and his voice erupted from it in deep painful groans. Frightened, I forced my eyes forward while trying to keep watch from my peripheral vision.

I smelled the garbage room before I came to its metal door. **GARBAGE** had been smeared diagonally down it in Jasper Moon (364-11). Drip lines from an over-soaked brush leaked at the bottoms of the two g's and the b. *Amateurish application error. You want to keep the paint brush well-fed, but not glutted.* But then, the paint applied—acrylic latex—was not even designed for metal substrates. I opened the door and activated its rubber door prop with my foot. A rush of warm, piquant air met me inside its concrete walls; and so did the old man from dinner. His head and shoulders were immersed in a waist-high recycle bin and he was prospecting for refundable plastics and tin. Uncertain whether he heard me enter, I spoke softly to avoid startling him. "Any luck?" I asked. Then I felt stupid. *He's not fishing for walleye, you stooge!*

But the old-timer hadn't heard me above the clash of bottles and cans and his aging grasp of sound. How did he manage to find his score? The only shreds of light in the long room were the ones I had escorted in. Otherwise he worked in utter darkness.

Recycling bins hugged the left wall and trash bags were arbitrarily flung to the floor down the right wall. Side-arming my contribution onto the heap disrupted a fat rat. The scrounger had been mining the trash pile and judging by its portly rear had not gone without for many a meal. He booked it safely to the rear of the room and I reacted as though half expecting his visit. *Yep, that's fitting,* I thought in calm resignation. I walked out of the room to the poignant rattle of discards behind me leaving the door propped for man and rat, each hard at task.

Could all of this really be happening? *This* day of days? I thought hard. Perhaps I had been admitted to a mental hospital. There were sharp clues to that reality: the floppy laceless shoes on my feet, the rubber band clasping my wrist, the empty parking lot (perhaps coinciding with the care facility's visiting hours); bare white walls in my bedroom; the jacket with straps Layne had given me; Layne's purple robe; Mark; Mrs. Holme and these crazies in the quad. Had I come from dinner in the psychiatric ward cafeteria? Was Kope an alter ego? Had I been committed? Was garbage disposal a patient chore and was I now strolling the grounds? Could I trust my own potentially-traumatized mind?

It must have been the job, I decided. Selling paint had finally taken the ultimate toll on me: institutionalization. And I knew which sales predicament had packed enough charge to make me snap. One of my painters ordered product from me tinted to some obscure colour. Then he found a low grade substitute at a cut-rate price and reneged on our deal at the last possible minute. Legally I was entitled to payment, but there arose ambassadorial concerns: those around sacrificing goodwill and future business. The old adage 'The customer is always right' won out and I, the coating salesman, was left with two hundred pails of Multi-Coat 3000 tinted Peach Cobbler (809-18). That must have been it. That was the straw that broke me, sending me here to Grandview Highway North Psychiatric Hospital.

I pictured myself hitting the brink. Stripping down naked and pouring buckets of peach Multi-Coat 3000 over my head. Rolling it on my skin with enviable technique. Cutting corners with a well-fed brush, covering every inch of my bare body with the required thickness outlined in our limited manufacturer's warranty. Then drinking a gallon: painting my insides. And right before I blacked out, paint bubbles popping at my frothing mouth, I would whisper: "The key word is value-added, people. Why buy a Camry when you can have a Hummer for the same price?!"

I debated checking the roadside for a Do Not Pick Up Hitchhikers sign, but my mind skipped diversions until I'd made it to my bedroom. There I found Kope with a look of deep concern on his face. He was sitting on my bed with head hunched over his suitcase and two neatly folded stacks of extra-large clothing.

"Layne went through my bag."

"What?"

"Nothing's missing," Kope groaned, lost in his own world. "Layne washed my clothes. He washed my *underwear*." Kope brooded. Like the small town rules for male hugging, men are also not to handle each other's underwear.

"My *underwear* man," he repeated, gazing at his briefs for a longer stretch. "Did you ask Layne to do some laundry?"

Fed up, I chugged the open Storm on my dresser and left to avenge not only Layne's encroachment on Kope's gitch, but all the rest of his bizarre goings-on.

THE LAST OF THE NATURAL LIGHT HAD BEEN PULLED away from Grandview Highway's arc on the planet and the once vivid living room now lolled in grays and blacks. As the hour came for electricity to shine at the end of my first day there, I had made acquaintances with seven area homeless, two resident junkies, Mrs. Holme, Mark, and a disease-ridden pest, but not yet the apartment's myriad of light switches. Deducing Layne's whereabouts, I slapped his door with three moderately forceful smacks. *Whap! Whap! Whap!*

Deadbolts his bedroom, but roams freely in mine like a dignitary, I thought as I waited.

"Yes?"

"Can I have a word?"

"Anytime buddy. What's on your mind?"

"Can we not talk through the door?"

"Oh sure." Layne unfastened the deadbolt and backup doorknob lock, and swung the door to an angle his boney frame could fit through, intently closing the door behind him as though there was a courtroom in session on the other side. "What can I do you for my friend?"

"What are you building in there, a nuclear weapon?"

He said nothing. I went to work closing the book on the first qualm: "I know you were doing Kope a favour, but those are his personal belongings. Way offside. And my bedroom is my only privacy, so, off limits. You get yours," I said, pointing to his closed bedroom door. "I get mine." I spoke sternly, rallied by a two-beer buzz.

Layne nodded.

"I took the garbage out."

"It's a pigpen, I know. I've been on Mr. Chin to…"

"And the crackies?"

"The what?"

"Druggies. Junkies. Crackheads. Downstairs. As we speak." What am I saying? I thought. This situation is absurd. This is a poorly written screenplay, an improv act, a news feed from a U.S. border city, a nightmare after a spicy meal. Not actual.

Layne referred to the guys downstairs as strays and called their presence a one-off. He tried for candid, but exaggeration plagued his delivery, resulting in a twang of insincerity; he spoke fluently, concisely and straight from a store of bull crap.

I allowed Layne his thin reasoning. Always easier in the short term to give third chances.

We were running late for Kope's Vancouver Experience, so I broke out the two minute drill for getting ready. I set the water temperature, tugged the shower lever, and a jetting of mist screamed down from the showerhead in a high-pitched *Hissssssss!* The pressure was there, as Layne had touted, but the problem lay in the fine, fire extinguisher consistency of the spray —a vapour similar to a prison delousing treatment. I waited impatiently for the water to moisten my majority, and cathartically scrubbed with bar soap, pissed off by this latest glitch and my earlier pow wow with Layne.

Eventually enough water ganged together to drag my lather down the gurgling drain. I whisked the rest off with my hands. Showering on the observation deck at Niagara Falls would have proven less time-consuming. And Kope hadn't mentioned the spritz, likely not wanting to put me off. Sloughing my chicken legs of the last soap, I sang my battle cry, Radiohead's Karma Police, looking to re-inspire myself.

This is what you get…

This is what yo…

This is wha…

When you mess with u…

Vaporous feathers tickled my throat, cutting short the chorus lines. I didn't know any verses, nor had I any inkling what the song was about anyway.

Finally clean and toweled dry, I stopped at the fogged mirror to brush my teeth. A peach miasmic blob cursed back at me. *A one-star chef couldn't muck a meal that bad. You are a monster f-up!* Ducking any backlash I cast my eyes down to the labels on my sink-side toiletries: 'Strong Hold', 'Fast-Acting', 'Fights', 'Maximum Control'. All at once life was proving itself too much for me.

Kope elsewhere, I stalled in my room. Lying on the bed in my damp towel, memories of Nic on Saturday night in Kits catching in my mind's eye. I clenched my jaw. Nic in her high black come-f-me boots, fishnet stockings, and a risqué blouse, face roaring Rebounding Hard! Her golden hair smelled of lavender, and curled in bouncy pockets down to her shoulders. Black eyeliner made the hazel eyes pop, cherry lip gloss dabbed the podgy lips.

Pinched nighttime air percolated through the mesh squares of my window screen, tickling my genitals. I was aroused against my will. *Remember, wanting her gives her power.* And stopping short of climax never did dam the guilt ingrained in me as a Roman Catholic boy. *Nic, undressed and lying flat on the bed.* I loosened the knot in my towel and attended to my resignation. *God watched you do that to yourself.*

Then I got dressed—lone pair of worn blue jeans that sagged in the seat, tattered trail shoes, a faded red golf shirt with a collar that leaned temperamentally left. My head hung low.

The living room furniture was lit up by a squat powerful lamp on a side table left of the sofa. The rest of the apartment was black as deep space. I had the sensation of peeking in on a theatrical set from the back curtain, blinded by the spotlights but sensing a considerate crowd in the near distance, powering off cell phones and swallowing coughs. Kope sat stage right and young Tommy, stage left.

"How was your spa sweetheart?" Kope teased. He'd tapped laughter from the unlikeliest of sources: timid young Tommy. Clearly, Kope had cracked the boy's shell with a beer and some kindly well-placed words.

"You need to catch up. Here Sally Struthers, chug this." Sally Struthers is the household name my St. Thomas crew would pin on someone—most frequently me—if they were acting sissyish. I later found out that Struthers, a television icon, dedicated her life to the interests of starving Third World children: it was an irony that had yet to thicken.

Kope rose to hand me a Storm and I marveled at his size. In time, people overlook the physicality of close ones, but Kope's sheer mass prevents that phenomenon. He had changed his clothes during my steam bath, deploying a pair of grey slacks, black belt with a large silver buckle, white silk button-down, and, new to me, designer eyeglasses with black rims. He looked studious and well-to-do and dressed to kill.

Layne beckoned me from the kitchen. "Nate, pal, can I clear something past you?"

I followed after him. The mild mannerisms that had shaped my impression of Layne had all but vanished, a shaky jumpiness left in its stead. His left hand jittered nervously as he bounced his weight from foot to foot, like a child awaiting escort to a public washroom. "Tom's in a bind. Thought we'd give him the couch."

"What? Layne, we discussed this. I'm on the couch tonight. Kope has my room."

His memory lapse vexed me, as did the moral anvil he had plopped in my lap. Do I want to house a homeless teenager I don't know from Adam, even for one night? Was I being selfish, reckless? Where do one's responsibilities begin and end? Give him the chair and a pillow? The floor and a blanket? A hug and a talk?

"My idea, my imposition. I'll keep him in my room." Layne spoke of the boy like a boarded pet. *Sure, just spread out dated newspapers and pour some water in a dish.*

"This sleepover idea is bad news. The kid is a question mark."

"Now Nate, you don't know like I know. It's harmless and it's one night and it's on me. We help the poor bastard and he'll be gone before you wake up. You wouldn't even have known had I not told you now. So, we're cool, bro?" Not a smidgen put out by having to share his bed, Layne seemed, in fact, practically begging for a green light.

Alarmed by the potential situation, I needed time to digest this news. Whether sinister or admirable Layne's intentions would culminate in impressionable underage Tommy slumbering in the body heat of a disrobed Layne. The onus fell on me to squash this idea. Onus was a four-letter word in my vocabulary.

"No. This is where I draw the line. If this is *our* place as you say, respect my decision." A bigger person would have added: "If you rape this defenseless creature, I will cut your pecker off and feed it to the garbage room rat." But the onus hadn't fallen on a bigger person.

Layne made a grumbling noise and walked out. I returned to the living room and the new tableau stung me: docile Tommy — Layne's foundling — taking strained sips of his adult nightcap; Layne, surly in his purple robe, stroking his moustache.

As we readied to leave, I sent Layne one last imposing look. "See *you* tomorrow Layne," I sneered.

Kope and I walked my grocery route to the mainline of taxis at Commercial and Broadway. The cool nighttime air and the change in scenery refreshed my senses. I put to rest the Tommy situation, convincing myself that even though Layne had already divulged his sneakiness, his grander intentions for the most part were pure. And hearing Kope point out that the kid had shown up out of the blue helped shelve any guilt.

We reached Broadway and Commercial and were hushed by the struggling souls—their numbers doubling at night—detained on stiff sidewalks. A crush of weekend traffickers was blowing through yellows and cutting one another off to the beat of off-pitch horns; a man sat strewn against a light post, clothing grimed with soot, cardboard sign at his side anchored by a string around his scruffy neck. Written in black marker, the sign read *I have a prolapsed colon and I am starving on the streets. Please give.* His face was tormented with red pockmarks and on the outside of his clothing, at his midsection, a colostomy bag bulged with feces.

My breaths grew short and tight. I felt ashamed for leading Kope to these people and ashamed for feeling ashamed of them. Living in Kits, I'd begged for realness, for a sampling of Dennis's 'sketch'. That realness now beggared me.

Kope flipped the rundown man a toonie, landing it perfectly in the cleft between his man-heap and his concrete bed. The guy appeared to be sleeping, but nodded ever so slightly when he felt the edge of coin hit its mark. I dug around my own pocket for change, but found only a five and kept it.

We turned west onto Broadway. A taxi driver spotted Kope's outstretched arm from the opposing lane and yanked his wheel for a squealing four-lane U turn in front of a slew of oncoming cars. This strike of luck and the cabby's wild stunt pumped our spirits, pushing thoughts of inhumanity to the back burner where Layne already stood at a rolling boil. I suggested a roundabout route into downtown that took us over the Granville Bridge. Granville Street descends amid low-rise condos to the water where the bridge ramps vehicles up and over False Creek. City racket deadens to the monotone of rotating tires shimmying over construction joints, and the water below is an endless mysterious black. The bridge bows, corraling its floating red taillights into a slit amidst the glow of skyscrapers. Its nighttime scenery rouses a sense of transcendence and impulse. And then you get down there and wait forever in line at a club, pay a hefty cover-charge, wait forever for expensive drinks, get hammered, eat street-meat, and go home alone to wake up hung over and you're still just you.

First we ventured a couple of the scuz bars Dennis and I preferred to the popular mainstays. Dim light over the pool table. Warped cue sticks. Green felt worn white, down to bare wood where the blue-spotted cue ball starts. Box of pull-tab lottery tickets on the bar (major winners fished out by the owner after hours). Open defiance of the government's ban on smoking. One beer on tap, referred to as 'Draft'. Pickled eggs and beef jerky in glass jars, selling for an even buck. Bags of plain potato chips humped to the wall by metal clips. *The Province* sports page under hard plastic above the urinals, dated by three weeks. Screw holes above the sink where the mirror once hung. Stall walls overwritten with poetic license. Pooled pee on the seats. Smell of anguish.

"Where do the Vancouver *women* hide out?" Kope finally petitioned, stunned that he need ask a newly single man.

Knowing the touristy clubs on Granville Street would gratify Kope's lust and grant me entry despite my footwear, we headed for the mainstream. Block-long line ups ran out of entrances like drool. Yards of people impatiently waited to dance to top forty music in their closet's best. I guided us to the end of the shortest line, strung from a place called The Roxy and accepted the inevitability of a forty-minute wait.

Kope refused to be herded. "Follow me. I want to try something," he said with wide thoughtful eyes, and brushed past the masses in a confident strut.

"We'll lose our place," I appealed in a Sally Struthers whimper.

Our drive to the head incited glowers and taunts from restless clubbers. Kope stepped to the doorman, neutralizing his accustomed size advantage. The beefy bouncer looked coldly at the two of us. *Whatever Calgary trick he's trying, it's not going to work here in Vancouver*, I thought.

"Quite a crowd you have on your hands," Kope said in his disarming voice.

The bouncer nodded, not warming.

"I'm not sure if we are afforded the same courtesies as back home...." Kope handed the bouncer a plastic card from his wallet. The bouncer scanned it, Kope's face, then the card once again. He looked unconvinced, but in the hand Kope put out to retrieve the card sat a crisp fifty. "From the boys at Station Four." Kope shook the cash, signaling the muscle-head to accept. His only job was to be big, count heads, use excessive force, and take bribes.

"Go on you two. Behave in there, I know how you smoke-chasers get." The bouncer signaled one of his crew to open the door, and cupped his hand over Kope's, refusing the money. We left the mash of people still in line wondering who the VIP's were.

Inside the front door behind a card table sat a magazine cover woman. My usual twitching ensued. "Cover is ten bucks," she sighed, eyes glossed over by routine.

"You drive a hard bargain," Kope said, perking the doormaid from her trance.

"You have no idea how hard," she cooed back, and bit her painted bottom lip.

"Maybe I should find out," Kope smiled.

The stench of cheesy adlibs is a bouquet you grow accustomed to around Kope. They have earned him the nicknames 'The Cheese' and 'The Laser'. The Cheese self explains; The Laser was born from a high school ski trip to Quebec. The class had been purchasing lift tickets at the bottom of Mont Tremblant from a cute French girl sitting in a heated booth behind a thick pane of glass. She'd spoken through a speaker, passing vouchers and accepting payment by means of a metal trough. "Dat will be turtee dollairs Monsieur/Madame," she'd repeated in a cute voice. I had paid and run for cover. Kope had stayed until he had her number written on the back of his receipt. A mighty feat considering she'd been at least three years older and behind glass.

"Impossible," Timothy Hines, a scientifically wistful boy from our year, had said. "Only a freaking laserbeam could penetrate that glass!"

A small crowd bottlenecked in behind us, ending my boredom. Kope gave the door girl a raised eyebrow and moved on.

The bar was packed well beyond fire code and the dance floor held together a sweaty mob in front of a large stage where a house band sandwiched sets of Eighties cover tunes between the layers of hip-hop pumped out by the house DJ. We found a free booth next to a cluster of women and Kope showed me the card. "My buddy back in Cow Town gave me his old one to fix up. Works every time." It seemed Vancouver and Calgary doormen were taking good care of their firefighters long before NYFD garnered worldwide fame from Nine Eleven; firemen everywhere were climbing the ladder from esteem to celebrity. I fingered the clear plastic over Kope's headshot, jealous of his savvy.

Feeling the squeeze of time and the looming last call for alcohol, Kope tripled his efforts. Within the hour we were on a first-name basis with the girls in the booths to the left and right of ours, and a circuitry nearer the bar had the pleasure of Kope's acquaintance. I was getting hammered on Crown, Kope ponying up for every bar tab. One wave of females had cameras, and insisted on shuffling in and out of the booth while Kope and I posed for snapshots. I overheard one of the girls say we would make a good advertisement for Big Brothers of Canada.

But I began running out of steam. I listened quietly to Kope's cheezy remarks at the table, as if I were his disproportionate bodyguard, and as the night wore on felt my periphery narrow into an alcoholic daze. The band, still jamming, deaf to my ears. The stage, the bar, the lights, the walls, the ceiling, the waitresses, the bigheaded bouncers, all one blur.

Layne slowly squirreled back into my consciousness. I felt as if he held both Tommy and I in his blackness. Blades of culpability that had been sharpening within my mind now found a clean sheet of ice to carve. Thoughts of what may have transpired while we were out slashed at my insides. Layne shrewdly fingering his moustache, stepping to Tommy, taking the beer bottle from his hand, replacing it with his tepid palm, saying: "Come now, Tom. It's time. It's time for bed. Come." The deadbolt slides into place.

I was near Tommy's age when the doctor repeatedly examined my privates. Twelve years old and hands pulling at my underwear. Thick thirsty fingers rubbing and prodding for clues. I knew first-hand just how out of breath you can be and how large the lump in your throat can get, I'd turned a blind eye. Left Tommy there under *his* guardianship.

The deadbolt slides into place.
The deadbolt slides into place.

I teetered on the curb while wrestling a hot dog, losing mustard out the back chute onto my jeans as Kope eyed the bar spill-out. Boozy and sexually pent up, Kope announced he wanted to conquer the Granville Bridge on foot. We trudged to the bridge and up to its apex while a parade of cabs zoomed past, each one leaving with stories from the thinning dimming downtown. The fresh air and hot dog served me well, and my speech returned. "Hey Cheese, remember watching Mr. Dressup at school?" I yelled over the flap of wind and whoosh of cars. An out-of-the-blue question after ninety muted minutes.

"Course, Mr. Dressup with Casey and Finnegan. Only TV I got was at school and your house," he said, distracted by the rush of suspended elevation.

"Think Layne has a Tickle Trunk in that bedroom of his?" I laughed a forced, maniacal laugh. Kope joined in, his more the polite confused variety. "He might just be filming a movie in there."

Lost, Kope stopped laughing.

"What do you think he'll name this next film?" I rambled on.

"Taxi time?" Kope asked. Not of me, but rather of himself or even a third entity, some grand overseer that might offer up some guidance on how to anchor his buddy's wavering state of mind.

"Nah." I said with a wave of my hand. "How about 'Tommy goes to College' or 'Dirty Dinner Party Seven: Pork On!'" I gave a half-blooded mutt of a sound.

Then I dropped to my knees on the concrete, scoring the skin on each knee, and began to sob loudly. Eventually I caught my breath to say "I just left him there. I'm sorry." To me it seemed a sweeping apology, spanning the six lanes overhanging dark water and whatever lay beyond. It was for Tommy and my feeding him to the lion; for Kope and a mockery of a first night; for Nic and the breakup I had not finished mourning; for Layne and the Grandview Highway fiasco; for me and my unrealized life. I cried, stiff sulks in the pedestrian lane on the Granville Street Bridge, succumbing to the stress of a turbulent day and two weather-beaten months.

Kope consoled me with his big mitt on my back. Then he led me off the bridge and into a cab heading east, where it was already day two in my new apartment and my crumbling crusade.

KEJA—NO, MARNIE—SLIPS INTO VIEW. I AM SEATED ON the middle cushion of the couch in front of her. Her funky dreads are tied back, exposing a steely smooth golden brown neckline. Would it taste of butterscotch if I pressed my tongue and lips there? Her white T-shirt is haltered, exposing the bottom curves of her heavy chest. **Ocean Pearl** lies in illegible folds below her throat. Her pink sweatpants have become a distant memory in favour of the panties (Cotton Candy 954-44) she is now wearing.

I awoke with a start, adjusting my eyes to the morning light. I started again when I saw Layne perched in the adjacent chair, book in his lap. I'd shrugged aside my duvet in my sleep, and lay exposed in my white department store briefs, my skin moist with broken sweat.

"Thought you were never going to come to," said Layne. His voice stiffened my lumbar as I scrambled for cover—a throw pillow, the bed cover, and finally, my shirt and jeans. How long had he been staring at my bare body? And Tommy. *Where's Tommy?*

Given the problem hangover sired by the previous night, I hadn't altogether realized that I spoke the words aloud.

"In the end, I decided to let him stay."

"He stayed?"

"I made a judgment call."

"A judgment call?"

"You were right, I didn't know him. But I knew his type. We were fine. Well, I was anyway."

"You were?"

"Sure, I had my bed. He slept on my old recliner."

"Recliner?"

Flipping answers into questions was not an interrogation strategy. I felt a depletion of bodily vitals, like a dropped drawbridge, that had inspired the pitiless onslaught of a migraine. Its palpitations marched with my heartbeat. Wavering unsteadily in my seat, I spoke to Layne with eyes on the floor to fend off the spins.

"He must have been some sore with those springs digging into his back. Poor fella. Would have had it better outside, mild as it was."

Sweet mother of mercy! He's not a depraved pervert! I exalted inwardly. You know you've fallen on hard times in communal living when on the morning of day two, word that your new roommate is not a pedophile and hasn't compromised an area homeless boy qualifies as a ray of sunshine.

"Look, I know it's not your bag, but I do have something for that head of yours. Don't worry. It's not crippler weed. This stuff is mellow. Cure you right up."

I saw submission as a way to keep our amiable morning moving forward and to reduce yesterday's iniquities to ash. Also, in two hours Kope and I would be registering the peal of the Vancouver Indy Speedway. My head needed a fast remedy.

Layne set down the book and went to work on a slender joint —he dubbed it a 'pinner'—for the two of us to burn. Too infirm to move, I waived the outdoor smoking policy and soon a grey spectre hovered above our heads.

The herbaceous smoke tickled my throat. I shortened my inhales to minimize my high and moderate my coughing with no success. Two rotations of the peace offering and I found myself in soaring contemplation of the damage crippler weed could do to me if this was mellow. Layne smoked out the rest and lit a cellared roach from some prior toking. His idea of a dessert course. My head pain soon conceded, as did the rest of my body. My thoughts took to wanderlust.

Wow, this couch is grrrrreat.

Am I sitting too low? What's the word? Er-go-nom-ically?

Look at my hands.

Are they always this white?

Maybe I've got the flu?

My knuckles are sooooo wrinkly.

Is that normal?

They look like tiny back catcher masks.

You haven't talked in a while.

He'll think you are phasing out, so talk.

Keep it light. Nothing to bum you both out.

Proof that you are in control of your high.

A simple joke.

Comment on the room.

Something in the room.

Make it sound spontaneous, but also clever.

Say it now.

Talk.

Anything will do now.

Make a noise.

Sneeze.

Cough.

Talk.

Talk!

I wasn't mellow; I was tripping out. Plucking words from the cyclone swirling between my ears and third-guessing their use, I had lost the ability to speak for the second time in twelve hours. Suddenly secondary were the brimming landfills, the e-wastelands of China, space junk floating in orbit, overtaxed fisheries and clear-cut woodlands. Combined, they didn't stack up to the world's greatest wasted resource: words. We talked and talked, but said nothing. We wrote and wrote, but inspired no-one. It was endless: tabloids, critical acclaim, acceptance speeches, P's and Q's, advertisements, empty promises, surefire excuses, legalese, racial slurs, bad jokes, memoirs, false confessions, paint industry jargon, the entire lyrical compilation of Celine Dion's 1990 album release 'Unison', lists. And yet. I could not generate one solitary word.

Layne filled in my hamstrung blanks with a signature head-scratching impromptu: "I checked in on the big guy earlier. He's sawing some heavy firewood in there. Snores like a bear in heat. Threw the blanket back over him and set two ibuprofen and water by the bed."

Mental note: Don't let slip to Kope that Layne tucked him in. Another: He left my duvet after I had shuffled it to the floor. The prospect of Layne ogling me curled my toes.

"Dandy weed eh? Look at these orange hairs," Layne said, gazing at a rotund ziplock baggie of pot. "I feel like a farmer going to the chicken coup to round up freshly laid eggs when I smoke my crop in the a.m.

"A night out getting whamo'd and a wake and bake. You must be famished. Like a castaway, deserted island eat-our-dead-in-desperation hungry," Layne continued, drawing laughter from me for a change. My first sound in ten minutes. "Can I scare you up some breakfast my dear friend?"

"No! Well, I mean, that is my stomach doing the talking. My stomach says no. I say yes, my mind says yes, but the readiness of my stomach…for food…says no. So no, says the stomach, on my behalf." Speaking suddenly felt like a baby's first steps.

I really wasn't hungry yet. As far as I was concerned, the fib Layne had told about being a trained chef in the upper percentile of acclaim was ancient history and we were starting new. So he lied. Big deal. You lie, I challenged myself as I painted Layne's lies Cirrus Cloud (711-11).

"I'm eager to learn your craft," I said, pointing in the general direction of his weed plantation. Trying my best to act casual.

"Cooking is easier than you think. Find quality ingredients, let them do the talking. I eat very little breakfast myself. Course, you lose the taste for it after your mother pulls out a loaded shotgun at the breakfast table and blows your dad's legs off," he said.

"Cheese and rice." The window curtain, drifting to saggy

breezes from the outdoors, slumped. Dust particles dancing in front of our faces halted. Smoke billows rolling the ceiling in search of porous escape dissipated. The faint beat of my heart pumping blood to the corners of my meagre frame, stilled. My spinning thoughts, my breathing, the vibrations, the here, the there, the before, the after, all came to a sudden soundless stop. Layne elaborated no further, instead reserving space for conversational debris to pelt the ground and my aftershock to take hold.

I sat silently illustrating my distress:

Frame 1: Shaggy-haired boy of six eats pancake stack at breakfast table in farm kitchen.

Frame 2: Obese woman in moo moo and apron fires obscenities at thin lanky man in jean overalls and red flannel shirt. Man spouts back.

Frame 3: Boy drops fork and muffles his pink ears.

Frame 4: Man stands as wife arms herself with loaded shotgun from pantry.

Frame 5: BANG!

Frame 6: Pellets mushroom from smoking nozzle and rip man's legs.

Frame 7: Blood splatters onto face of boy.

Frame 8: Man's upper half drops to floor.

Frame 9: Gob-smacked boy watches.

Frame 10: Man screams incessantly.

Frame 11: Woman's basso laughter tripped by coughs from inhalation of gun smoke.

Kope surfaced, drawn in by the silent commotion. Long in the bathroom, he was suffering from an affliction of the rye drinking set: whiskey bum.

"Morning." Kope reached his arms to the ceiling, stretching out the last kinks of sleep. "I need food, you?"

"Kope, I can whip you a hungry-man brekie in two minutes. This Sally's too woozy for eats." Layne now took it upon himself to use our insider quip—addressing my friend with the name given him by only his closest childhood chums.

"That is a tempting offer Layne, but you know when you are on vacation somewhere how you crave dining out. The experience of it all. You know." A more eloquent excuse than my 'tummy says no' defense. Kope unhooked himself from Layne's offer with the poise and promise of a man who overruns sales quotas.

"Think restaurants, Nate. We leave in ten," Kope told me.

"I ride shotgun," called Layne.

I languished in unwieldy discomfort sitting kittenish in the back of the Chrysler behind Kope and Layne. In my last conversation with Layne, he had told me about the time his mother mutilated his father with a long gun. In my last conversation with Kope, I'd cried like a baby and gobbed wet snot on my shirtsleeve. This car reeked of new interior and unfinished business.

Kope sidled the 300M past the same broken down Pontiac 6000, alone again in the crumbling lot, and into Sunday traffic. He shifted gears like a pro, channeling the excitement of race day, decelerating from breakneck speed at the last possible second. Layne held onto his door handle as he would a flotation device during a plane crash at sea.

Step on it Kope! I boosted silently. I felt none of the Indy pep, I just wanted Layne in our rearview mirror for the day. How dare he invite himself to our pre-Indy breakfast! I hated him. I hated him for delaying my catching up with Kope. I hated him for smoking me up with high-test stash before exhuming his childhood. I hated him for exposing my sheepishness—a braver person would have challenged his ungodly claim. I hated him for sabotaging his limited role in the simplest of plans. I hated him for yesterday, for today and for the tomorrows at his disposal. I hated Layne for the guilt I felt in hating him, for wanting to sling him from the car by the hairs of his moustache, watching his eyes bulge like a jigged walleye.

Quick remorse for these sadistic thoughts gently returned Layne to the front seat where he held onto the door handle for dear life. Hunger, headache, lethargy, gastrointestinal distress and triangular pensiveness caused conversation to lag. Kope tried to get Layne going by commenting on his T-shirt.

"**Vancouver Sun Run**, eh? You ran?"

"Who, me?" Layne said. A facetious smirk lit his face. "No sir. Running is for people who have nowhere to be. This is just some T-shirt." And that was it for conversation on the way to The Meat Wagon.

I knew The Meat Wagon well. A place where I'd often attended morning meetings with painters; forced to watch subhuman life forms, multicoloured speckles on their coats, slurp eggs and dip white toast in coffee. The Meat Wagon's proprietors advertised the place as 'not your garden variety joint', their shtick being that you could not find any fresh produce on the premises. In place of a tomato or cantaloupe slice, plates arrived with a garnish of orange and watermelon wedge candies. The house special was a hearty portion of steak and eggs called 'The Slab and Scramble' and omelets were prepared 'meat', 'cheese', 'meat and cheese' or 'plain'.

The interior was wallpapered with anti-vegetable propaganda posters. One I can remember read 'Fork Salad!' with a picture of a garden salad and a fork with all its prongs bent down except the one in the middle. Newspaper and magazine clippings, set under glass, boasted the health benefits of a diet rich in red meat, made popular at one time by dietitian Henry Atkins, whose portrait also had been hung in reverence. The only hint of vitamin C on the menu was in the Beverages column. The house conceded to offering a glass of orange juice in a smaller font than the other drinks, but added an asterisked warning: 'Not Recommended'. Newcomers brazen enough to ignore the caveat and order the juice discovered in time that it came, with a jeer from the waitress, in a four-ounce tumbler—one-third the size of the other beverages.

True to its promises out of the many seedlings I'd planted in painters' heads in the booths at The Meat Wagon, rarely did one germinate into an actual deal.

The rest of the place fell in line with my style, or lack thereof. Its signage was simple: an old Coca-Cola logo above plastic slip-in letters. Their menu was streamlined and their prices reasonable. Swivel chairs lining a countertop. Deep-set booths. Pecan pie set under plastic lid. Drip coffee only—nothing cinnamoned or whipped. The same two scraggly waitresses with hoarse voices. Short-order cooks. Hand-written bills. Cash only. No frills. Come as you are. Breakfast in Nic's Kitschylano would've meant a truly big line-up and the joint would have a hip name like Eggistential or Great Eggspectations or Hash. Hungover self-important twenty somethings would be dressed to the hilt, drinking mimosas, forking over fifteen bucks for a plate of free range omega-3-enriched eggs, seed toast and slices of heirloom tomatoes.

On weekdays the bulk of the clientele were tradesmen somberly swilling coffee and mapping out their workdays. On weekends I found all walks of life filled the seats, and in numbers as random as a room full of Lotto 649 winners. The three of us squeezed into a tight space against the wall behind two groups of three already waiting for tables. I had never lined up to eat there before.

My muteness carried forward from the car. Kope said "Busy", Layne said "Yeah". The waitresses zipped frenetically around —the quickest I'd seen either of them move—and the cooks turned orders so fast that the smoke coming off the grills looked as though it was discharged from their metal spatulas. I stood against the wall hungry, but enjoying the personality of the place. Like a subdued friend who'd been rambunctiously energized.

We were second in line when Layne's fidgeting broke our quiet spell. Face tensed red, breathing hard, he scowled at the backs of the man, woman and baby ahead of us. He stirred in line and let out exasperated snorts, jostling with stagnancy like a rodeo bull in a bucking chute.

The young couple and child got seated, putting us at the front of the line. But Layne had hit his brink, and began vocalizing his distaste.

"What's so special about this shit hole?

"The food looks ass.

"Any idiot can crack an egg.

"This waiting is bullshit. For a couple *sloppy eggs!*"

"Settle down, alright. What's the problem?" I said.

"The problem?" Layne spoke over the noise in the room, loud enough so that diners seated near us could hear.

"We're next," I added.

"Next? The problem is half of these shitheads are finished. They're just sitting there, sucking on coffee refills. Here's the concept: Order, eat, pay, fuck off," Layne said before drawing a cigarette from his pack. "Jesus Christ. You two can wait here like a couple of idiots if you want. I'm *outta* here!"

Having heard Layne's outburst, the people in line had cleared a pathway to the door for him to storm by. Out he went, slapping the door open with two-handed force. His noise had grabbed the attention of many inside, heads turning to the exit like a flock of disturbed Canada geese on a golf course fairway. I stepped through the still-parted lineup and opened the door to watch his progress. Much as Kope had done mine in grade five.

"Is he waiting by the car?" Kope asked from the front of the line.

"No. He's walkin' home," I answered, stupefied.

One of the waitresses stepped to Kope. "Alright love, table or booth?"

"Booth please," we affirmed in harmony.

THE MOLSON INDY VANCOUVER IS AN ANNUAL race in the Champ Car Series that attracts over 150,000 spectators over three days. Drivers will roar through the streets of Vancouver and along the banks of False Creek at speeds of up to 300 km/hr. The 1.8 mile curvaceous road course will test the most technical of racers this weekend with clutch-grabbing hairpin turns. For more, visit the Race Technology Showcase at Science World.

I had decided we'd take the SkyTrain to give Kope another vantage point of the city.

When we arrived at the venue my eyes adjusted to the sun's reflection as I read the information board posted inside the main entrance. I was biding time while Kope asked a Miss Molson Indy contestant in black and white checkered tights where he could find the Chrysler-Dodge party paddock. He was also asking her how her day was shaping up and if she believed in kismet. I moved on to the next panel.

Greg's Spirit Shines On.

Greg Moore, born April 22, 1975 in New Westminster, BC, started racing karts at ten years of age.

At age 18, he became the youngest driver to win a CART-sanctioned event, placing first at the 1994 Indy Lights Phoenix.

The next year Greg was an Indy Lights record-setter, taking 10 of 12 checkered flags, including five in a row and walking away with the 1995 Indy Lights Championship.

At age 20, Greg graduated to Indy. Highlighting his rookie campaign were a second at Nazareth, a third at Cleveland and a fourth in Toronto.

At age 22, Greg became the youngest winner in Indy history, capturing the checkered flag at Milwaukee in June of 1997. He won at Detroit the following weekend for good measure.

At age 23, Greg won in Rio de Janeiro and bested the field at the U.S. 500 in Michigan. Greg signed a three-year contract to drive for Roger Penske.

At age 24, Greg Moore was killed in a crash at Fontana, California on October 31, 1999.

Greg Moore 1975-1999

His spirit shines on.

The Greg Moore Foundation

A sobering picture of fresh-faced Moore in his racing coveralls topped the caption. This fated young man—a year older than myself—had been cut down in his prime. I consoled myself with the thought that some, including me, would kill for a prime to be cut down in.

"Not the bimbo you would make her out to be. A feisty one," said Kope, nudging me back to the land of the living. "At least she knew the grounds."

"Sure she did. It's a requirement of a Miss Indy hopeful to know her riding."

"We're not far. Beer ahoy!"

Mr. Kopic & Guest dipped around general admission racing fanatics on course to our corporate seats. The exhaust from food stalls watered the insides of my mouth. Foot-long hot dogs, rolled to a plump brown, tantalized our senses. Cotton candy machines spun melted sugar into the air as proprietors wound lollipops of wool in purples, blues and pinks. Fluffy popcorn squirted with salty butter, crisp golden french-fries showered in salt and ketchup, apples suffocated in gummy caramel—a junk food blitzkrieg. I gave thanks for the virility of the heat wave that had us in golf shirts, for free time with an ace of a friend and to the many distractions diverting me from my mounting life worries.

Being confined to a small package, I had perfected the art of scampering and would regularly need to wait on Kope to lumber a path through the crowds. I delighted in this rare advantage over him, but eventually we found the guarded Chrysler paddock and this time gained entrance without posing as Calgary firefighters, to explore the inner sanctum of the racing spectator elite. Inside this capitalist's playpen cookie-cutter blondes dished imported beers and erections to businessmen, as they stood around in candelabra formations upping each other's stories. An overzealous Chrysler employee manning a barbecue pit cheered us over to indulge in his steak sandwiches.

Hands full of beer and meat we slid down the row indicated on our ticket, the ductile metal floor rattling out our progress. National anthems commenced the moment we were standing in front of our empty seats. As if the mishmash of advancements and delays, the hurrying and procrastinating, the stop and go, the Laynes and the Nikkis, since our births, had led us to those two seats at that precise moment in time.

"Fluke timing," Kope said, reducing it to mere coincidence.

The emcee called on the drivers to start their engines. Bursts of pent-up horsepower riled the crowd into a frenzy.

Vroom-vroom.

Vroooooom.

Vrooom.

Vroom-vroom-vroom.

Vrooooooooooooom.

Forgetting our food cooling in the seat shadow beneath us, Kope and I and the rest of the VIPs sat on the edges of our padded seats—equipped with cup holders and complimentary programs—until the green flag waved and the Molson Indy Vancouver 2001 class of cars sped past the Chrysler paddock into turn number one. *Nnnneeeeeyyyooooowwww. Nnnneeeyyyooooowwww. Nnnnnnnneeeeyyyowww.* Their electrifying sound was unlike anything I had ever heard.

"Whooh! Go! Go!" I cheered, catching myself off-guard with sincere excitement at the outcome.

"It's so different live," Kope pointed out, all fired up.

The drivers skirted turn number one without incident and the twenty-six car field sped off to tangle with the rest of the 1.8 mile course—one-hundred times over. Spectators urged on their favourite drivers, most backing Canadians Paul Tracy and Patrick Carpentier, futilely screaming at our two countrymen who, sound blocked by the high-powered motors, helmets and radio headsets, couldn't hear a word of it.

Approximately ninety seconds later the racers passed once again, this time having created distance between them. This spread widened as the race wore on, and smaller groupings began to pass at random.

Two cars would pass.

Then one car would pass.

Then three cars.

Then one car.

Then two cars.

Then one car.

Then four.

Then two.

Two.

Three.

One.

Two.

There were instances when cars would stop in the pits for certain racing amenities such as gasoline, tires, and tune ups. Most times they just kept going around and around and around.

On lap twenty-nine the track announcer declared that Canadian Paul Tracy had been ousted from the race due to a light, but day-ending, crash. Our private box let out a collective sigh—a Very Important Pout coming from our special section.

Neyow! One car passed unnoticed.

Kope and I passed the time with stories of simpler times back in St. Thomas and new ones from our respective western cities. One triggered the other like tumbling dominoes and we traded them back-and-forth as we once did baseball cards—some new, some doubles.

Neyow! Neyow! Two cars passed unnoticed.

The die-hards on hand that day, the ones who know of and appreciate every little detail that goes into the design and production of an Indy race car, who know and respect the positional, financial, and most importantly, human costs of collisions—if they could have read my mind for what I thought next, they would have mobbed me. *One where nobody gets hurt.* I thought, pleading for carnage. *A turn one bash-up would make my day, but don't bounce a tire up here.*

Neyow! Neyow! Neyow!

Three cars passed. The third had the same colour scheme, baby blue and white, as the one Greg Moore posed beside in his memorial at the entry gates. The memory of his fair complexion and smiling face now accused me. *Is it a crash you want? Is it really?* it said. Killed in a race on his tenth lap, his car smashing into a concrete wall at a speed of over two hundred km/hr. A death witnessed by a handful of family members, a live audience of thousands and a television audience of millions.

"This has got to be, without a doubt, *the* most boring sporting event in the history of mankind," Kope said, finally voicing the sentiment I had kept harnessed in my head for seventy-odd laps. "Let's head."

Drunken giddy, we joked on our way to the outer gates, down the streets lining the banks of False Creek and onto the up-escalator to the SkyTrain launching pads. As we waited for the eastbound train, we gazed out of the glass enclosure to the city-encroached waterway. Salty ripples had shucked the obscurity of open ocean to die with distinction at land's end as False Creek waves.

A SILVER HANDRAIL, SMUDGED WITH THE FINGERPRINTS of thousands, separated our seats on the SkyTrain car. We sat facing the passengers on the other side and the visuals over their shimmying heads. The final scenes of our Indy experience on the waters of False Creek flowed through the gulches of buildings, passing like filmstrip in the window; snippets of backcloth flickering faster as the train reached its crowning speed. As whitish-yellow sun mellowed to an afternoon orange blush, pockets of urban foliage and the colourful hides of painted buildings shed their reflective blare and showed off their truer colours.

Kope gave way to a power nap. Left to myself I read an article in my Indy program sponsored by the Vancouver Historical Society, about the naming of False Creek: the once undiscovered non-discovery. Imagery flooded my head like a Foley Falls dam break, streaming me back to 1859 as Admiral Sir George Henry Richards navigated his HMS Plumber into the oceanic branch of the then unnamed-by-Europeans creek. Richards was conducting a hydrographic survey of the coastlines for the Royal Navy. After inspection of the surrounding seaboard, he supposed the creek to be an extensive inland waterway and a channel to valuable coal deposits.

Then he reached an early impasse and discovered the river

was nothing more than an aquatic cul-de-sac. So Sir Richards decided to cut his losses by setting sail, and tersely named the disappointing inlet 'False Creek'. Little did Sir Richards know that beyond the deadlock lay a wealth of resources not in fossil fuels, but in timber. Nic and I had this thing we did in bed. Face to face she would feel for my toes and rest her two feet squarely on the tops of mine. Confident in her alignment, Nic would press on the gas, compelling my feet down, upon which I would jack hers back horizontal, like a gear-shift on a motorbike. Exactly opposing, balanced pressure—me pulling her up, her pushing me down—we made a connection. I'd conceived a deeper meaning to it during the headier times. The formation represented the two of us, different in our approaches, meeting in the middle to be one. I now saw this game for what it truly was: two mulish sucks out to prove their mettle and impose their wills. We left ourselves a future unnavigable by bitter end. Our hearts, undiscovered unmined coal, had proved a False Creek of our very own, stopping well short of any promised land.

Kope slept greedily. The steady travel of the SkyTrain, high above embattled street traffic, nudged him deeper and sounder. Not even his tinkling cell phone woke him. The track curved northeast in its nonnegotiable route, making memories of the train yard and drab buildings on the aptly named Industrial Avenue. Clark Road and the Grandview Viaduct filled in rolling scenery; I looked ahead at Layne. When would it be time to cut my losses? Had the time arrived? Would it be as clear and curt as water to land? My teeth went to work on my nails.

Bushed from the day's half-assed end, one in a lifetime of half-assed endings, and done in with rehashing Layne troubles, I resigned myself to the conversation across the aisle. A man put together like a variety pack of highlighters—lime green plastic sunglasses, yellow turtleneck, fluorescent pink wind jacket, baby blue wind pants, cream gloves and snow white running shoes with thick orange laces—had boarded at the previous stop and was imposing a tête-à-tête on the stranger in the next seat.

Trapped, the crestfallen woman gave in to common courtesy. His eyes, his message, his wrappings, together spoke of a mental disorder. I sympathized equally with both captor and captive.

"You know how many fingers touch these handles, honey bunny? Only about a bazillion...*Balls falls*," the two-word incongruence leapt from his lips in a parrotlike yap. His bobbing head and colourful plume made him seem a mimicking bird. "Think about the germs squirming along these bars. What's on people's hands? *Balls falls!* I'll tell you what, honey bunny, anything from dirt to fish food to sweat to boogers to spit to blood to doggy doo-doo to holy water. Lord love a duck! *Balls falls!*"

The lady managed to frown and smile at the same time. My response was to woozily remove the fingernails from my mouth.

As kids, before compassion took to us at varying ages and degrees, we callously wrote off the mentally ill, calling them retards and bloopers. Now, opposite me, this nervy man garnered conflicting sentiments of pity and envy. What instigated his fear of infestation? What is '*Balls Falls*'? Did something happen there? Is there a connection to his germ phobia? But I also envied him his delusion. It was flamboyantly clear that the man existed in an alternate reality. One day—at birth or otherwise—he boarded a mental escape-pod and fled. Retreating from a complex world of poverty, hatred, materialism, genocide and terrorism. His world was one where your only enemies were micro-bacteriological, and fluorescent was fashionable.

I flicked my gaze again, letting the advertisements near the ceiling guide my thoughts as the track did our course. The bewildered man became a wisp of unfinished business.

Now Playing: The Lord of the Rings: The Fellowship of the Ring
Simon Fraser University: Creating Opportunities Together.
Canadian Bible Society: Sowing God's Word.
werent2U.ca: Find a great place to call home.

The SkyTrain map over the doorway read like any other advertisement, endorsing the plenitude of terminals I could have moved to: Refrew, Rupert, Nanaimo, Joyce-Collingwood, 29th Avenue, Metrotown.

"The next station is Commercial, Commercial Station," a monotone pre-recorded female voice announced.

Running side by side with Grandview Highway North, the train pressed on above wild overgrowth around the track base until the train window framed my apartment building. A scarred, spinning head, rotting wood balconies sagging from the second storey doors like bags from tired eyes.

Looking down on it, I felt the pure sting of regret. I pretended I was a visitor in a city zoo, cosseted in a monorail car, safely observing the untamed Animal Kingdom in their paddocks below. The rust-crusted Pontiac 6000 sat alone in the lot like climbing apparatus for a featured creature. Abruptly, I imagined the lady's voice from the train's PA system guiding my imaginary zoo tour.

To your left is the compound for The Layne or cannabis craziticus. A feral carnivore recognizable for its thick band of whiskers above its upper lip, this cunning hunter blends into its habitat with plain clothing and inert behaviour until ready to strike, when it opens its retractable purple coat and attacks with spastically timed, paralyzing thrashes causing social confusion. The Layne survives primarily on the hallucinogenic buds of the flowering cannabis plant and some studies suggest this predator may copulate with its young.

As can happen with zoo creatures the doors to the cages were closed and no animals emerged from hiding. But there would be no refunds given, as stated on the grammatically-challenged tenancy agreement posted at the start of the ride.

The train's wheels whirled my building from sight; a shack that commuters assess on their way home to cookie-cutter subdivisions. Plagued by curiosity, they ask themselves questions: "What poor souls live there? What are the goings-on in such a hovel? Why doesn't the city tear that down and rebuild?" They shift in their seats, relieved at their insulated stations in life.

"Commercial, Commercial Station," the woman's mechanical voice announced one last time as the train slowed to make figures of blurred crowds on the platform. I roused Kope from his power

nap, taking pleasure in fathering him off the ride through the disorientation one gets in the seconds after waking.

Down the escalator and through a tiled passageway, we were spit out at Broadway and Commercial. The scene carried on unhampered: traffic lights changing red to green to yellow to red, two lanes of motorists verging on the junction from four directions then making haste away from it in different directions, the sun slanting down unfettered, and the people lying in waste. At the far corner I side-stepped the piece of concrete where the man with the plump colostomy bag had been parked the night before, but not without a tremour of shame.

We were nearly home when Kope noticed his vibrating cell phone and retrieved his message. "It was Nic," he revealed.

"What's she want?" I asked, feigning disinterest, all the while flexed and rushing on the inside. Kope pushed a button and put the phone directly to my ear as though it was my first time using one. I took it from his hand. The phone had a sleek design like a vintage cigarette case and had good face-feel too. *"Sent today… April second…at…four twenty…p.m…new message from…an outside caller…twenty-three seconds."*

"John, Nic here. What, you fuckheads don't call? Bako is in town. Dropped in unannounced. Fucking typical." Another mutual friend from back home, Bako (balk-o), had originally said he couldn't make the trip down from Whistler due to a lack of funds. Kope had offered to pay Bako's way, but he had refused. Told Kope to f-off. "Come by my apartment, say nine o'clock," Nic's recorded voice continued. "We pre-drink, then go to a classic resto-lounge down here. You retards are in deep shit for not calling me."

I reinserted a germy fingernail into my mouth.

WE PUNCHED THE INTERCOM CODE AND WAITED FOR

Nic to summon us into her building's prim foyer.

"Yah?" a deep, diced version of Nic's voice asked.

"It's u-us," Kope broadcasted into the mesh.

"Duh-uh." Nic mocked. "We have you on the TV security chan-nel."

I looked up and then swiftly, self-consciously, down. *Oh to be back in the taxi, in that transitory limbo, that state of neither here nor there.*

Deep breath into the elevator; deep breath out of the elevator. The long fifth-floor hallway—floored with vintage hardwood (Oolong 165-97) and a runway carpet (Belgian Chariot 754-32)—had the warm heavy smell of church. At the end near Nic's door slept an antique oak table with a porcelain vase centred on its top. In the vase's belly stood a posy of showy pink chrysanthemums, the perennial prize planting in my mother's hobby garden. These were real flowers, staged with a wiry weave of some yellow bush like tumbleweed.

Trying a bit hard aren't we? I editorialized, green with envy.

Door #513 was unlocked and opened onto a cloakroom with faux marble tiling. A framed black and white photo hung on the wall above a red rubber shoe mat pictured a woman in formal wear—high heels, flowing gown, pearl necklace, Josephinian gloves—dramatically shielding her eyes with her forearm. She was blocking from her sight a pair of muddied work boots on a sullied nearby patch of white carpet.

In from the cloakroom ran plush Polar Hug (678-75) carpeting, to a kitchen with a pass-through, and a rear hallway. It went on to bedrooms and bathroom. Straight ahead, the same carpet ran under an iron-and-glass dinette set and to our right, the apartment's common room.

The layout provided only momentary distraction from the loud yellow paint on the walls. It was so bright it had voice. A squealing, panicking voice. *Whaaaaaaaaaaahhh*, it cried. A shade of yellow that rarely leaves the colour sample wheel, the swatch must have read 'Chernobyl II' or 'Afterlife', and been swaddled in a mantle of dust. *Surely this has to be accent paint*, the technician in me first said; but we entered to see the same merciless retinal plague plastered throughout the entire apartment. Timothy Hines, that scientifically wistful boy from our elementary school who'd dubbed Kope 'The Laser', would have called it the closest man-made reinvention of a gamma ray.

Nic had indeed ordered furniture for her new place from the IKEA mega-store that had recently opened in Port Coquitlam. It was furniture she could not afford, but bought on credit because there were certain amenities she had to allow herself. Port Coquitlam soon gained further notoriety for pig farmer Robert Picton, allegedly the most prolific mass murderer in North American history. He eventually stood accused of luring prostitutes and heroin addicts from Vancouver's East Hastings to parties at his farm, butchering them, and feeding their remains to his pigs. I cannot rightfully infer a link between the Picton massacres and the IKEA mega-store, but if not submersion in a cesspool of consumerism, what drives people to commit such acts? Then again, what drives Celine Dion to such wondrously heinous melodramatics on stage?

Nic yapped from a couch named EKTORP while her fetching roommate Cassie swayed in a gaudy rocking chair named GUNGHULT. Bako lay in hiding somewhere. On their coffee table next to a large vanilla-scented candle sat the same pewter frame that Nic had displayed in our basement sublet. It held the same photograph of a young girl flashing a bright smile in full ballerina costume complete with pink bodice, slippers and tutu.

Nic had been a Big Sister to this girl for the past six years, ever since Jess was five. Nic had added the 'Miss' to make her feel more special, like a princess. The endearment so touched the girl's mother that she warmed to calling her daughter Missy instead of her original pet name from birth Jezebel. Miss Jess's deadbeat father had long ago gone away and her mother had several names for him that he could never change.

The move out west had been hard on all of them. No more sundae-factory movie bonanzas, pizza-by-the-slice backyard firework displays, or miniature golf go-karting arcade adventures. A tearful Miss Jess presented her Big Sister Nic with the photo and frame at a small going away do her mother had put together. The sad-eyed little girl made Nic promise to call often and to display her photo where Vancouver people would see her.

Nic reluctantly kept her word. She hadn't been embarrassed by the photo. She loved Miss Jess. Loved seeing her happy. It was the kudos for sponsoring a needy child, which inevitably followed inquiries into the large photo of the pink ballerina in her living room. Those were what aggravated her. Nic felt the commendations tarnished the sanctity of her bond with the girl. Any charitable aspect of their friendship had long since been shed: she gave and Miss Jess gave back. At the same time occasionally people would also comment on how impressive it was to see a young girl studying ballet, whereupon Nic would respond "Miss Jess? Oh fuck no. She's just a touch on the slow side."

"The fuck took you guys so long?" Nic said around a wad of purple Hubba Bubba. She kneaded the cud with short chews and blew two hard bubbles back to back: *Furrrrrrp...Pop! smack, smack, smack. Furrrrrrp...Pop! smack, smack, smack.*

"A little downtime after Indy madness," Kope said, over-embellishing the thrills of the afternoon.

"You two fucks have lost it since high school," Nic said.

"Speaking of high school, you girls serving beer along with

those wine coolers?" Kope bit back, mocking the fruity spritzers in their hands.

"Em, cheeky wank," Cassie said in her raffish Scots accent, tantalizing Kope with seductive dips in the chair and a huntress smile.

"Sorry sugar. The abnormally big one with the *big mouth* is John, and the wee one is Nathan. Guys, Cassie," Nic announced. My lips curled back into my mouth as I gave a restrained nod. Kope's response was two gliding steps and a genteel handshake.

"Charmed, Cassie," Kope said.

"My friends call me Caz. All, em, but Nic here."

Another signature of Nic's was that she refused to acknowledge anyone by a nickname or pet name—which everyone has in a town like St. Thomas. She addressed people by their legal names only. It was done not out of respect for the parents or a hobbyist's interest in etymology, but rather to be different.

"Oh pullease John. 'Charmed'?" Nic said. "And don't slag off our lady drinks. You two are in the shithouse as is, leaving me here to deal with Mike the tosser all day." Nic thumbed at the sliding glass door behind her, which gave nothing away but a dimmer reflection of the caution-yellow room. *Slag off.* I noted her adoption of Caz's U.K. slang.

Kope scouted out beers from the kitchen while I grabbed us chairs from the dining table.

"How was the bus ride over here?" continued Nic to Kope, though I was ten feet from her.

"We took a cab!" Kope hollered through the kitchen porthole.

"Wait. Back it up. You took a taxi," Nic said, shocked. I knew immediately where she was going. "Holy fuck! John, you *must* be a champion salesman, convincing El Cheapo over here to spring for door to door," she cried. Then suddenly aware that open aggression towards her ex-boyfriend could be interpreted as insecurity, she flipped from bedevilment to exaltation over her "fucking fantabulous" apartment and sexy Scot co-renter Caz who made a rabbit stew for dinner that was "fucking unreal".

With full beverages in our hands, conversation hit its stride. Caz talked about Aberdeen, Scotland and her depressing "ghet" of a job at a staffing agency. Kope briefed us on Chrysler and Calgary. Nic slipped in apartment features and Kitsilano wonders, including a story about the barista at Starbucks who had a "mega crush" on her and only charged her the Short price for her Venti. My attention wavered from this social weigh-in. Snippets of conversation seemed to fall around me like hair trimmings onto barbershop linoleum. I reverted back six hours to Grandview Highway North.

Once inside my front door, the day's Indy fluidity of colour, sound, movement and drunkenness had been thrown to languorous greys and inert blacks. My balance had failed me despite the familiar surroundings. As if disembarking from a carnival ride, I'd perceived myself in motion when I wasn't. I wavered on my feet, fumbling with the textural simplicity of unlacing my shoes.

Unsteadied still, I'd climbed the stairwell, which seemed to inhale and exhale on my ascent. It was breathing Kope and I in as though it were an oxygenating creature. I'd slipped on the last step and my shinbone had clapped the stair's metal capping. A delayed spill of pain had leached from my leg to my core, unsettling my stomach.

"Careful," Kope had said helpfully.

I'd fallen up the stairs, so that my disproportionate shoulders and beanie head were in the apartment while the rest of me was out. I looked set for the guillotine. Feeling a cool run of blood slowly tickling the hairs on my right shin, I knew I had a matching accessory for the raspberries on my kneecaps from my pavement breakdown the night before. I glanced into the room. *Who's this now?*

Tommy, of all people, was plopped on the couch in his clothes from a day ago, a lit cigarette and Hustler magazine in his hands, and a measure of junk food—cola, potato chips, chocolate bars— set on the coffee table. Just another hormonal chap settling in for a mid-afternoon tug on my sofa.

"No smoking inside. Number eight in the tenancy agreement," I barked, not knowing what else to say.

"Phssss." Tommy sounded his displeasure and rolled it over with his eyes. He discarded his smoke down the mouth hole of a soda can where it hissed its death in the backwash.

"Is he here?" I said, twirling my finger.

Tommy looked me square on, cold stones in his sockets. "The hell do I know? Do I look like his keeper?" He turned back to his Sunday reader. I could hardly believe this emboldened creature was the same kid. Popeye on spinach, Scooby-Doo on Scooby snacks. So I let him tell me off, this neglected child with a sore neck and no roof.

I'd knocked on Layne's bedroom door—locked, no answer— and stepped past my bathroom, catching the pong of Kope serving time on the toilet, before I'd identified the change jar missing from my dresser and realized what it meant. I was benefactor to Tommy's binge.

What was Layne doing leaving that rogue unguarded? And what do I do now? Shake down a hungry teen? Confiscate his porn? Say to him: "Bad Tommy"?

While I'd considered the impossibility of the situation, Tommy had corralled his junk stash and fled. I'd locked the front door after him and escaped into a power nap of my own.

I'd awakened to the glowing red sticks on my alarm clock floating nine-three-one at the space where my dresser had once stood. Day had passed into night unattended. Memory and feel had shepherded me to my lamp.

Kope had seen my lamplight and come to my bedroom, ready and raring to go, having showered while I slept.

"I just talked to Nic. She said to come by after ten, give her time to sort out her business. Bako is there bumming around, waiting for us," Kope had said eagerly.

"Right. Nic and her *Business.*" In the name of sounding important, Nic referred to any errand or To Do as Business. Any task, no matter how menial—taking out the garbage, changing a light bulb, picking up milk—was catalogued this way.

I'd tried for a rousing shower of my own. It had worked, in a way.

My fingernails had been chewed so far down that the skin was breaking its seams and the shower head's microscopic shoots of water drilled into the raw exposed flesh, sending hotwires of pain to my elbows.

The genial even-keeled Layne had returned in my sleep. He apologized for his earlier neurosis at the greasy spoon. "It's the crowds and the waiting and the noise. I don't deal," he'd said, all the while rolling us a joint to take with us despite my refusal. Like a soldier assembling his rifle, he'd welded it in seconds flat. "Lick and stick. There! Professional tip, if I may: Zig-Zag papers over Johnny Player's every time. Nine out of ten stoners agree," Layne had continued. "Now, in case of emergency, light and suck."

I'd accepted the party favour on my friend Bako's behalf, nestling the white stem in my jeans like a newborn baby chick even though I knew it was more like cradling the venomous Australian box jellyfish. Waiting for Kope to re-reconfigure his hair, I'd reported Tommy's thieving to Layne, who had also discovered both pot *and* gold of his own missing.

"You were right Nate. I should have listened. But don't you worry, that little swine will get his. I'll make damn sure of it." A mischievous look had transfixed his gaunt face. Silence had compressed the room. It seemed Layne couldn't go without crazy for five minutes.

Kope had finished his hair and we'd guzzled the last Storm. Layne, it turned out, had reserved some of his best lingo for our final goodbye. "Thinking you boys will need a lumberjack breakfast after all this boozin' and titty-titty bang-bang," he'd yelled from the top of the stairs. "Remember: wrap up those pygmies."

I'd grinned up at him painfully before closing the front door on his unhinged laughter.

Spoiled with the craft brew at home, Nic's name-brand swill— marketed around its Canadiana and 'drinkablity'—went down with an antacids-in-water smack that dented the reputation of the world's oldest alcoholic beverage. "Give it the trunk test.

Taste it warm. If you can stomach it out of the trunk, it's good pop," Dennis would have said. This beer: Fail.

The patio door slid open to the squeak of rubber on glass. Past Bako's shot-putter legs, I threw a quick look at Nic's terrace and beyond before the door slid shut. Arrested slightly by the view, I reworked my posterior into my chair.

Bako turned to face the four of us. It was good to see my rough-cut friend, fresh from his easy village life. We were more friends by association with Kope rather than true buds. In his brown Burton hoodie, whitening from wear and smelling of hash, jeans on their last legs and a sun-bleached red ball-cap with brim horseshoed and low to the eyes — looked the part of snowboard bum. Bako stalled his progression inside as his eyes went to the ceiling and a hand went down to his crotch. He never readjusted his bits in the universal guy way of a general shake-up. His approach was unapologetically meticulous. In this particular case, he couldn't help but chronicle that his left-side testicular sack was gummed to his shaft and his underwear liner had rode up into the space provided. With every eye on him, Bako stood correcting himself as though he was signing to a deaf person. Somehow normal to all in the room but Caz.

I had also grown accustomed to Bako's compacted head that seemed bigger near his jawline than at the top. To me, his head looked like a ball of Play Dough squashed to his body. It never hurt him in the lady department though.

"As I live and breathe, it's team dildo! I want to thank you two assholes for leaving me alone with this hair-bag loser all day," Bako announced, flicking the back of Nic's head with his hulky fingers.

"Ouch, Mike! You fucking wanker!"

"Suck my fatty-fat-fat."

"Eat me."

"I don't eat at buffets."

They carried on like a two-man stevedore crew on smoke break. Throughout high school I'd coveted Nic and Bako's friendship, linked as they were by their brash inside jokes, their indecipherable cribbage lingo (fifteen-two, fifteen-four and six is ten and one for the Johnny?), their Players Extra Light King Size cigarette co-op, and their joint addiction to the Nine Inch Nails' song Closer to God. Back on the eve of Nic's move to Vancouver Bako had tried to warn me about her history with men: a tobacco tradition of chew-spit-replace. I'd gotten defensive. "I didn't ask you, Bako! You know, I'm not some stranger who just rode into town." Echoes of teenage jealousy reemerged after having been made to feel like their outcast once again. Of course I'd apologized directly after.

"Great friend, shitty girlfriend. That's all I'm saying guy," he'd ended.

Very soon I was to fulfill his prophecy, becoming just another lump of Nic's used chew.

"Em, slug that tosser Nic!" Caz called out.

"I love her accent! She's so Trainspotting," Nic said. I saw an eye roll from Caz.

"Listen darlin'—Caz, is it?" Bako called back. "I'm going to need you to clean up that peasant English." Bako took some getting used to. In his youth, Bako, like me, had lolled under the canopy of Kope's protection. But unlike me his affliction had not been stunted growth. Side by side, we three were the beverage sizes at a fast food joint. Bako had won his bull's eye around a sharp and loose tongue. He could rattle more chain than a fleet of tall ships dropping anchor in deep sea. My all-time favourite was when a bully from our rival school had called him an a-wipe, to which Bako'd replied: "Well then you must be the dirty asshole they sent me for." Full-blooded Croatians in a tight ethnic community, Kope and Bako made early ground in a longstanding friendship. They were candle-bearing altar boys at the Croatian Catholic church, teammates in Little League soccer, playmates on the Croatian summer wedding circuit, and coworkers in the stomping of grapes for house wine or the stacking of apple wood for smoking meat. In high school the two tracked girls like bounty hunters tracking criminals, and they always got their perp. Bako was handsome like Kope, but not in the pretty-boy Beverley Hills

90210 sense. His look had an edge that put girls on notice. He also rounded the brim of his ball-cap in a horseshoe shape and wore it low to his eyes, which I thought cool. But despite his glowing track record Bako constantly beefed about Kope stealing the top one percent away from him, calling Kope out as a swindler, snake, and "hotness nabber".

I valued Bako for everything my friend Kope was not, though Kope was not lacking. Where Kope was tactful and clement, Bako was brassy and impulsive. It was his mother who had given him the play name Bako—derived from the archaic Croatian term for bull; coincidentally, 'bako' in Hungarian means 'executioner' or 'axe man'. But Bako was unfiltered homebrew. In a stereotypical world, Kope and Bako were the friendship pairing of a London museum curator with a cattle-drivin' Texan.

The type to attract branding, Bako is also known by the name 'The Keeper of Souls'. In high school Bako used to make drunk people sign over their eternal souls to him for cigarettes, beer, rides or whatever party essentials they were desperate to procure at the time. A typical contract would read: *I, Paul McCoubrey (Coubsy), hereby give my undying soul to Mike Baric (Bako) for two cigarettes and a Labatt Blue.* Bako had had a shoebox under his bed full of such contracts, written on beer labels, empty cigarette packs, ATM receipts, and napkins: his own spiritual slave trade papers. It would drive Kope nuts.

Also worth mentioning is Bako's storytelling jocularity, especially amusing when he's working plots for the blockbuster movies. I get to hear them all, followed by him trying to convince me to write his screenplays. He talked up this brainstorm last year:

"Picture it guy, a group of buddies just like ours. You know, they should really base a movie on us."

"This isn't like the one where the fish are fishing the humans, is it?"

"For the record, the fish are *humaning* the humans. And no, butt-suck, this is different. Picture it, a circle of dudes jumping on the marriage bandwagon. The usual story, one friend bites the bullet, then hush-a, hush-a, they all fall down. The honeymoons end. Wives fatten and turn into demanding she-bitches. Green nighttime facial masques, toilet seat nagging, no time for the boys, in-laws, plus shoes, shoes and more shoes."

"Oh those shoes."

"Shut-up. So, whining over beers with the crew, one of the guys compares wedlock to jail: no sex and no escape. Another, the token alpha, adds that at least in prison you get three squares a day, prison yard basketball, TV without Oprah, radio without Celine Dion, time to work on your delts, peace and quiet. 'And conjugal visits,' the token fat friend says. 'Wild, depraved, visitation sex!'"

"Wrote yourself in Bako?"

"Shut-up Midge!" Midge was Bako's nickname for me. "This is primo and you know it. So..."

He'd paused to gather his thoughts and tug at his gonads—tangled and pinching pubic hair above his left testi. "Without getting into the short and curlies, they plot a crime to get themselves thrown into jail. They try to break into prison. They blunder a few crimes by getting away with them, cash and jewelry stashed around the house for coincidence—no, for fluke...for—"

"Irony?"

"Yes! So finally they get the book thrown at them by some funny old judge, cameo'd by a klutzy Chevy Chase or a super-baked Willie Nelson, hot boxing in his chambers and shit," continued Bako, now in full-stride. "They soon realize that prison life is not for them—say after someone gets shanked, or raped, or the food sucks—and try to break back out. Funny, right? I've narrowed the titles down to Jail Bait, Wed Lock, or Prisonscape. What do you say, guy? Help me write the thing?"

Bako and I hugged at a slant, standardly bent at the waist like two halves of a little kid's crayoned house. He elected to give Kope the bird instead.

"How's mountain life Bako?" I asked. Slow and steady I presumed.

"Smooth Midgie."

Bako had moved from St. Thomas to Whistler in 1999 and was leasing a one-bedroom loft in Creekside. To offset a letter's market, Bako had suckered an impressionable Swedish backpacker, Sven, into subletting his lumpy couch for $750 monthly.

"Anything in the works Bako?"

Bako always has something in the hopper and he eased into his latest abstraction, a nature short. As he did so, Kope made four chair leg indentations in the carpet nearer to Caz.

"Picture it guy, three hung over pigeons on a boardwalk, eating from discarded fast food wrappers and rehashing the night. One gets ridiculed for banging a pelican. *Damn! Look at Cheese work!*" Keeping tabs on Kope's progress with the fair Caz, Bako's pitch had gotten choppy.

"Alright, scene changes to three hung over dudes, same boardwalk, same banter. Guy gets ripped for banging a—*Fuck, I saw her first. That's dibs every damn time. Fucking snake,*" Bako hissed, wandering again. I was getting the out-of-sync monologue of a prom chaperone.

"Okay," Bako resumed. "Three dudes kick the pigeons out of the way. Say: 'Stupid shit-hawks!' Birds take exception, say: 'Stupid humans!' Birds dive-bomb dudes with morning-after diarrhea. The Beatles 1995 reunion track, *Free as a Bird* plays as the birds take flight in slow motion. More up-tempo music and faster tracking when they open fire, say *Surfin' Bird*, by The Trashmen."

"I don't know about this one. It may offend some people."

"What? Picture it guy: dudes are caked in projectile shit, running away to 'Bird! Bird! Bird! Bird is the word! Papa-oom-mow-mow. Papa-oom-mow-muh-mow!' It's genius! We could call it Fly Over, you know, like hang over. Or Bird-Boozin', or, or…"

"Pigeonscape?"

"Step into my office Midge. — You're fired! Douche."

WE FOUND OUR WAY TO NIC'S FAVOURITE KITSCHY
lounge with six vowels in its name. Clearly there was a
discriminatory hiring process favouring busty size-zero
waitresses. Pricey international beer list. Snack menu including
Thai spring rolls and Ahi tuna sashimi. Fireplaces and leather
couches. Wood-trimmed walls airing out from the recent bylaw
banning smoking in pubs. Disinfected bathrooms with video
screens over the urinals airing ads for body spray. Automated
self-cleansing toilet seats that rotated after every hands-free
flush. Polished billiard balls, brushed red velvet, matching red
chalk. Smell of affluence.

We ordered five cold pints of draft, coloured Pale Straw (521-
31) to Amber Locket (090-05).

My shot. Missed again.

"Try using the lady's aid, Midge," Bako coached, kicking at
the bridge hooked to the wall like a samurai sword.

"It's called a *rest* Bako. And you say I don't know English?
Stupid fool," Caz yelped.

As a whole, we were a fashionista's nightmare. Nic wore
a skimpy black dress that made her look like a prostitute and
made the rest of us, except Kope, look boarded up. She was
overdressed for ten-dollar-an-hour pool, but appropriately

dressed for a revenge reunion with an ex. Legs as smooth and tan as boomerangs ran down to her barstool foot rest in a coffee-one-cream bend. She'd crimped fast curls around her face with playful hair pins. A silver necklace she never used to wear hung around her neck. Trophy of a new life.

My shot. Missed again. Caz had me by six balls—skunk territory. Ever more emasculating was her nonchalance in doing so. Engaging her four onlookers in Scottish folklore and lewd sheep jokes as she stretched out over the red felt into her next shot. She snookered me behind her solids and handcuffed me against the bank as an afterthought. She did it as easily as if she were tidying her room while gabbing on the phone, and punctuated her sentences with the crack of made shots.

Even if Caz had me dead to rights, during her waits for me to miss Kope supported her delicate sparrow wing of a hand, demonstrating his gentleness in showing her an effective bridge posture.

"Bend your index like so and bunny-ear your thumb," Kope instructed, showering her with attention. Caz giggled and Bako's face crumpled as though his lager had been laced with his pee.

In fact my friends' romantic dead heat had devolved into a one-horse race when earlier Bako had relieved himself on government property during our walk from Nic's apartment. He 'broke the seal' on a red Canada Post mailbox.

Unfortunately Bako's urinary tract operated in the same main vein as his mouth. His bladder was insufficiently sized and for this curse, he saw the world as his own personal urinal. Also carded 'The Mad Whizzer' by those in the know, he tended to pee whenever and wherever the yen grabbed him: behind gas pumps, under picnic tables, in laundry sinks, below football bleachers, off balconies, on church lawns. His closest friends had each been accidentally urinated on.

"Bako! You incontinent horse-fuck," Nic had hissed under her breath after hearing the hollow rap of pee on the letter can. Too late. Bako had pissed himself in the foot, so to speak; Kope and Caz had been mutually coquettish ever since.

When still coupled, Nic and I had kept our eyes from

wandering: mine with no place fairer to roam, and hers dutifully restrained. In our heyday Nic had had a catty panache for ending the glom of the many flirtatious men who'd said to themselves 'No way they're together!' She would widen her eyes and mock her admirer's stupour, or cleanly jack her middle finger, pantomiming an 'F-you' for her predator. But now I was back of the line and the flight of stairs to the co-ed bathrooms near our table were drawing a migratory stream of competent men. The first keeners passed by unengaged by Nic. She kept her eyes blank, a reflex from the decorum of days gone by. Then came a change. Slowly she recalled her state of singlehood, like a landed fish let off its hook and released into open water. Gingerly floating at first with hook wound still fresh. Then a wary fin flap, no resistance. Then ramped, tumultuous freedom. One of the more fetching of the lavatory-bound guys even received a gamesome wink for his troubles. A simple twitch that subjected every tissue in my chest to a hot wrenching.

Crack! In went the eight ball.

"Bring on the next sheep!" The amusement of billiards staled and testament to our aging logic, we decided on dollar drinks at home in place of seven dollar drinks at the pub. Kope commandeered the cheque. Caz was aglow with gratitude. Bako, though desperately low on funds, sat torn by resentment.

Amply drunk we walked back to Nic's in the formation of a five-roll on a die. Kope and Caz in front, then Bako, then Nic and I in back. Getting along famously all of a sudden, Nic and I razzed Bako—traditionally the agitator—from behind. A cordial glint of days gone by and time irreparable came over us.

Fading back from the pack, we traded jibes for old times' sake. "What gives with the ratty bracelet?" asked Nic. I had flipped Tonya's gift inside out to hide the inscription. Nic and Bako can be a mean one-two punch and they would've had a field day on me. "Looks like a piece of extension cord."

"Gift from a new neighbour," I said, undisturbed.

"Suits you," she jabbed. "Speaking of which, you still rolling tubes of toothpaste like party noisemakers and pressing slivers of soap together into new bars?"

"You ration jokes just as well, I see."

"Look at you. I know these clothes are second-hand, so is there a third-hand shop for you and Dennis to donate to? Say a Goodwill II store? You dirty fucking hippie."

"Me? Add some fishnets to that black tea towel of yours and you're hooking down on Pender."

Giving me her middle-finger face, Nic shot right back. "Right. I'm getting style lessons from you, The Greasiest Hobo. Why don't you pucker up and kiss my ass. Better yet, how about one on the lips?" Nic stopped, snatched my hand, and guided my body in front of hers. The white neon streetlight above us smoothed and whitened her face so that it was flawless as a geisha's.

"Kiss you?" Caught off -guard, I could not have sounded more unsure of myself.

"Fuck yah, let's be bad," she whispered, combing her curls behind her ears to clear me a runway. Her breathing sped, double-D's testing the integrity of her spaghetti straps with every heave. "Kiss me like you never have!" she demanded suddenly, eyeing my lips.

"You want one that bad?" My attempt at playful torment came out straight, like a bank teller repeating the amount of a deposit.

Nic pulled me to her by the bottom of my shirt, so close I could feel her round parts on my chest and her thigh slink between my legs. A cornucopia of malicious fights from our recent past flashed before me as I contemplated locking on to her wetted lips. Any fallout would be worth the attention, I hastily concluded, and drew in. Our mouths were near enough that I could feel her grapey breath on my chin before she fish-hooked my mouth away with two bent fingers.

"No. Stop. We can't," she sighed.

"What?" I said, but it came out Rah.

"Do we want to open that can of beans?" Her now steady breath reeked of premeditation, entrapment and bad acting. "We mustn't."

"Mustn't? What are you auditioning for, Shakespeare in the Park?"

"Be serious."

"Me be serious? A second ago you were demanding a kiss, next you are jigging my face like a friggin' walleye. I think I taste blood."

"Fuck me, I'm sorry," she said, again lame and unconvincing. Curls falling back over her face.

We walked in silence for the remainder of the moonlit push home.

Finally making her building's front walk, I turned to her.

"It's *worms*! Open a can of *worms*!"

AUSTRALIAN ABORIGINAL MYTH SPEAKS OF THE MOON
and the sun being created by supernatural creatures that once slumbered beneath the earth's surface, in a condition known as Dreamtime. The sun was feminine and the moon masculine. The moon influenced the fertilization of women, plants, and animals, and was regarded as husband to all women. If a girl feared getting pregnant, she took care not to catch the attention of the 'Moon Man' or look at him too closely...

Nic's top floor balcony had plenty of room for their gas barbecue and two Adirondack chairs. Its foot pad was clean concrete and the railings artistically molded wrought iron. Her building was the tallest of the Kits low rises, and boasted a view of the rooftop patios in her hood. They were draped with lanterns, white icicle lights, and tiki torches; in some, residents entertained guests, taking in the night sky with drinks and tapas. The view held the ambiance of an exclusive club: an elite treetop society with shared access to the sights.

The clear night sky, rammed with stars and a cotton ball moon, came into lucid view above the streetlights. One night from fullness, the moon reflected enough sun to dance on the water and mark the mountain peaks in the distance. Streetlights polka-dotted the dark rise of West Vancouver across the inlet and to our right a jutting of hydroelectric glow spoke of a downtown waterfront hidden from view. The flicker of jaw-dropping scenery lay bare before my eyes. I felt grateful and deflated.

Nic, Bako and I, leaned against the rail and breathed in the scenery like three drunken pigeons on a wire. The other two pigeons had taken travelers from the fridge and left a sticky note that read:

At beach!—Caz & John

"How is that streaming cluster of stars our galaxy, or solar system, or whatever? How does that work?" I asked Bako or Nic. I ask the same question of the Milky Way every time I see it. I also never get an answer.

"Bet you that weasel is eating blood pudding right now. Fucking Cheese," Bako grumbled.

"He better not defile my Cassie, or I'll fucking lop off his sack." Nic kinked the line of smoke rising from her cigarette and took a hard drag—a telltale sign that she had drunk past her limit.

"I've heard that most of the stars you see from Earth have already burnt out. We are seeing the travelling beams of dead stars," I said.

"Easy Astro Boy," Bako told me, along with a punch to my arm that sent the neck of my beer down the front of my shirt. Nic cackled loose and slovenly for three seconds and then coughed for six. "Hey, is your new pad top secret or something? I asked Cheese earlier and the wad tells me to ask you myself. Fuck's going on Midget?"

"Oh right. The nutbar," Nic added, feigning forgetfulness.

"Nutbar? OK, out with it guy," Bako demanded.

I had somewhat prepared for this. First, I revealed the joint from my pocket and we smoked it. "Yure no tokerrr. Where the fffuck you get thish?" Nic slurred. Once her diction forsook her, she was ten minutes to blackout. I could set my watch to Nic's after-party stamina.

"This particular strain came from my laundry room."

Joint blazed and appetites wetted for a story, I fought off muteness and gave them the original, unedited version of my

Layne Story—the accomplished leg of it anyhow, including the early segments I'd kept from Kope. "*Thasso crazzzy.*" These were the only words Nic, now an inebriated pile, could marshal.

I placed my hands on her bare shoulders and tried to link up with her dipping eyes. "Nic. It's time for bed," I said.

Eyes three quarters shut, Nic complied, feeling her way through the lit apartment, bumping into furniture like a pinball. Bagged from his day too, Bako motioned to the couch. "We'll talk more tomorrow," he said, pinching one of my nipples through my shirt before going inside.

I stayed on the veranda a turn longer. My drunken, stoned mind rolled over frivolous observations: Layne's longish fingernails, the birthmark on Bako's neck, Caz's arm hair, Nic's drink choice, the smell of rosemary hand soap from the bar washroom, Mark's shoelaces, the height of the curbs on Grandview Highway North, the butchers at the Safeway. The murmur of Layne's heat lamps, face of Bert's watch, the dust settling on our overstock of Super-Coat 1000, the slogan on Kope's Alberta license plate. Images whipped around my head: a panic attack of the inconsequential. I suppose a defense mechanism of the cowardly.

A large ocean freighter, carving a crest to open sea, crossed the bay and bellowed its horn. *To be on that departing ship. Neither here nor there, and on my way elsewhere. Wake smoothing itself behind me, gone without a trace.* The slow blink of its deck lights both teased and encouraged me as the boat set off for elsewhere.

Balling myself under a thin blanket on Nic's carpet, I pictured Kope and Caz's escapade. I'd thought I'd detected a gleam in her eye for Bako, and she did seem to be arguing with him a lot. I finished their night in my stoned head: cold sand squishing between their toes, Kope and Caz would kiss passionately on the beach. Caz's breath would smell like rabbit droppings. Kope would handle her face and nibble her lips as if they were lettuce peeking out of a giant cheeseburger. Struck by the fancy that she was just another notch on his watchstrap, Caz would deny Kope further physical advancement. Kope, having falsely associated her abrasive manner with sexual liberality, would receive one tenth the burnishing he was accustomed to. On that warm April night in Vancouver, the females would disprove Aboriginal myth and reclaim the moon.

NIC AND BAKO HAD INSISTED ON SNOOPING, SO WE
all rode over in Caz's car. Layne was concerned when he met our
assembly of five at the top of the stairs.

"Hey bud. Oh there's a whole flock of you. Big crowd for a
Monday," he said, fervently scratching the back of his neck in
discomfort. He mentioned the day of the week as if it were a holy
day of obligation.

"You see the circus act over on—Broadway, is it? What a
clusterfuck," Bako whispered to Kope.

"It's somethin'," said Kope safely, looking at me looking at
Layne.

"Well it's definitely not nothin'!" Bako said, peeved. Bako
would often misread Kope's tastefulness as an inability to call a
spade a spade.

Layne managed to balance himself through the introductions
and eased into a cordial normality, inviting the three 'newbies' on
a tour of the space—one that would include the longest laundry
room stop of any real estate Open House ever. I squirmed
when Bako addressed Layne at first shake as Layner and when
the three gawkers, taking pleasure from my pain, shadowed
him on a narrated sightsee. With Broadway and Commercial's
ragged people and the sorry state of the building's exterior in

recent memory, they drank in the yardsale decor, the botanicals in the back room, and Layne's two o'clock bathrobe. I've heard Nic fuddle with sayings that suggest sleeping in self-made beds and not crying over spilled milk, but I have yet to hear one that recommends giving guided tours of your blunders. Room to room, Nic must have thought me the biggest of a-holes. A self-inflating grin rode her proud face.

Mistaking our purple jacketed guide for Willy Wonka, Bako petitioned for samples at every stop in the walk-through. "You think you can break me off some professional grade toots? Some powerhouse Club turbo? Eh, guy?" At every shameless request, Nic went as red as her fingernails (Four-Alarm 777-72) and with them nipped the fatty skin at Bako's tricep. Caz laughed smartly, enjoying Bako's edge more and more by the second.

Even though the door to the rotted balcony lay open, the air in my bedroom was hot muck. "What are you going to do?" inquired Kope, speaking over the trim folds of clothing he was packing away for his ten-hour commute through the Rockies. His voice was concerned and grim. His words were said about the room, but his spacey eyes were mulling over the visit. Each stowed article became another page turned in his mental scrapbook.

"Leave here," Kope said, snapping out of his pondering. "Quit your job and move to Calgary. My VP tells me the housing market in Calgary is ready to explode because of oil demand. 'Juicier than a mechanical bull at a strip club,' he always says. Good guy to work under. I can get you a job with Chrysler," he went on. "Work hard, save for a couple years, and buy some property."

Bako blew into my room just in time to rebuff Kope's offer. "Shah! A fine job working eighty-to-a-hundred-hour weeks. Just give your soul to the security guard in the lobby for a keycard. Or are they retinal scanning at that empire of yours? Huh Dope?" Bako paused for effect, like a lawyer in one of his screenplays. "Screw the briefcase trumpeteer, Midge. I say stick it out here. Sure Layner is gonzo, but those plants are going up like rockets. Buds the size of my cock in four to five weeks." Bako clawed a bud of B-52 Bomber from the baggy Layne had finally given him and sniffed it with glee.

"Keep it down! He eavesdrops," I hissed at Bako. "And trumpeteer is not a word."

"Ride it out?" Kope piped in. "This coming from a guy who can't hold down a job longer than two months."

"Barefoot Bistro in Whistler, Assistant Busboy, three months strong. Great staff discount and hot-as-balls waitresses," Bako said, winking at me. "At least I'm free of the corporate dog collar and not trading youth for the right to eat gravy from the clammy hands of fishy old men. No way. I'm a stone child of the earth, man."

"Beatnik poetry in motion, *man*. Spoken by a guy whose better days consist of sharking foreigners for his rent, carving fresh powder and hustling couch cushions for change to buy KD."

"*White Cheddar* KD. The crown jewel, guy," Bako interjected.

"Watching *Goodfellas* for the millionth time on his twelve inch, bunny ears change-the-channels-with-a-butter-knife snowboard stickered piece of shit."

"'*What am I a clown? Am I here to amuse you? Tell me what the fuck is so fuckin' funny about me!*' Joe Pesci. I love that movie, guy."

I laughed at Bako's weak impression. Both of them were on a roll.

"Right Bako. Then go ashtray diving for roaches."

"Hey, at least I'm not waking up at fifty with the realization that I burned away my youth sucking wrinkly ass behind a big desk."

And on it went: my left-shoulder devil and my right-shoulder angel in a sermonic dustup. Cause for concern had they not been at odds since forever. Neither ever conceded victory in this fifteen-year stalemate. This time, in my eyes they were both right; Kope in his suit and trench coat, Bako in his hoodie and snow pants. One unrelenting, chasing the golden goose; the other floating on a cloud, stealing time with the simple life before it got serious on him. What the hell are men in their early twenties *supposed* to be doing anyway? Fighting terrorism? Starting families? Backpacking Australia? Dying in race car accidents? Battling fatal diseases? Selling paint?

I waved good-bye to Kope from the walkway. Layne gave the rock-n'-roll salute. Bako flipped the bird. Nic folded her arms. Caz kept the previous night's cards close to her chest with a simple nod. Kope would drive ten hours straight home, steal four hours of sleep, and put in another twelve at the office. As he backed his car out from the building Kope gave me a tight rueful look through the windshield. Probably the same one he wore that day in grade five as he gazed at my muddy struggle through the schoolhouse window. *I'm sorry to be leaving you like this*, his look said—and added, in this case, *but not sorry to be leaving."*

Layne excused himself to the back balcony to smoke the last of his B-52 Bomber. Having had their fill of sketch, Nic, Caz, and Bako decided on home. Tired from a late night we all said weak goodbyes. Bako made Nic and Caz wait in the car as he came back to my bedroom to talk a turn longer.

"Gotta ask, do you think that Cheese sealed the deal with Caz last night?"

"Not sure."

"I don't think he tapped it."

"Why?"

"My trick knee."

"Hunh?"

"Every time that poacher steals a chick meant for me, I get a sharp pain in my left knee."

"You are severely bent."

"It's true, guy. Not only that but last night I had this dream. Caz and I were dancing at a nightclub, her tight ass in leather, perky tits in sequin, hot as fuck. We were grinding on the dance floor when a massive wrecking ball smashed through the wall and swung directly for us. I pushed Caz aside and it passed between us, missing by inches. It demo'd a glass bar on the other end of the club, shards flying everywhere, and came back our way. On its backswing I noticed that the wrecking ball was Kope's stupid dough-head on a chain, laughing crazy at me through those big horse teeth. I unleashed my samurai sword and cut the Kope-head from its chain."

"Wait, hold up. You had a ninja weapon handy?"

"Samurai weapon, yes."

"There's a difference?" *And you recognize it.*

"A major one, yes. Ninjas wear all black and fight with nunchucks, stars, and smoke bombs. Samurais wear colourful robes and fight with swords and staffs. Ninjas can kill a group of guys coming at them at the same time, but for the most part they apply stealth and trickery. A lot of night raids. Samurais, having more honour, are day fighters, needing to see the whites of your eyes before making a kill."

"Boy they're like night and day those two."

"Ha, ha, not funny. The Kope-ball was twice my height, so I jumped up and severed the link."

"You can't even hop a fence."

"Can I finish? The chain was the Kope-head's lifeline so it stopped laughing, went grey, and died. I dropped the sword, grabbed the chain, hooked Caz with my free arm and swung her through the hole in the wall to safety. It got a little weird from there, but I think the dream and my trick knee not going off are signs that stupid Cheese got cock-blocked."

"Sounds like a movie script. I can see it now: 'Discoscape!'"

"I own the rights!" Bako cried out, in fear of my pen. "The ladies are waiting so I'll say what I came back here to say: you're doing it again and it kills me to watch."

"Doing what?" I defended.

"You over-think everything. And don't feed me that look, because you know it's true. Your eyes tell it all. They're everywhere. Stressing about this, that, and the other. Nic, work, Layne, life.

"Look, Nic is Nic. Top friend, worse girlfriend, worst ex-girlfriend. Work sucks, but work sucks for everybody and you're coping. And Layne," Bako lowered his voice, "he is bat shit crazy, but he's harmless and this dope deal is good for us. Layne's got the free pass. It's airtight. Listen guy, fact of life: you can't get laid without getting your little wang wet."

Meeeeeeeeeeeeeeeeeeeeeeeeeeep! Caz's off-key horn, held for extended bleating. I imagined Nic's whitened fingertips, and her indignation. Before I could compile a caution, Bako stepped onto my balcony to give her both his middle digits. The balcony protested with that crescendo groan that preludes structural collapse.

"Whoa, whoa," he said in panicked laughter, drawing back to stable hardwood. I, the one on solid ground, was more shaken than him.

"Our time is up. Nic is a testy bitch and Caz wants my bod. Remember, stressing does nothing but taint a perfectly good buzz," Bako said in closing. "Treat your problems like a bag of 'shrooms: take them in doses. That way, you don't trip out and start to think that your shirt is untucking itself."

He gave me that spacious, sun salutation man hug, and off he blew. But not before, in his unorthodox style, he had made me feel a great deal better about my predicament. I think.

ALONE, I SPENT INDETERMINATE MINUTES STANDING next to my bed mooning over the effects distance has on friendships. Dissecting the moments of reunion, nosing for evidence of lost connection, and fearing the worst. At long last I corrected myself with Bako's parable about magic mushrooms and therewith, the need for a nap overcame me.

My body took to the bed like acrylic primer to cedar shakes. Weightier aspects of hosting Kope over-with, slideshow of Nic's fresh start having run its reel, and a night of back-wrenching sleep on the floor endured, I slept a calm drooly sleep in the sparing dark behind my eyelids, for the better part of three hours.

The dead sleep righted my head. Invigorated and clear, lying belly up on the bed, I spread out my mental papers against the ceiling (Lacey Pearl 006-56) and went to work on a bright side. *Layne is a solitary man, a rogue lion,* I tried. *He prefers his world slow and regimented. Layne was unready to live in communion with another, let alone house a third, even for a short amount of time. Like an only child trying to entertain their parents' dinner guests, overwhelmed by the adrenaline rush of having an audience, he overreacts. Why can't I make that childlike comparison? Is it so preposterous? The man has a fort for a bedroom. Throws tantrums when things don't go his way. Bullies the other kids. Keeps his money in a drawer. Smokes weed from colourful toys. Enjoys a good sleepover*—I was opting to embrace the better and discard the worst regarding Tommy—*above all, battling serious disease at a young age loosens anyone's mental stronghold. How is a man supposed to act on the recovery end of cancer? The only health crosses you've had to bear are a dairy intolerance and a fussy left nut. What life obstacle have you bowled over? Who are you to judge him?*

Flat on my back, I intuited that Layne would settle into a calm, albeit curious, normalcy once he relaxed into our situation and the parade of tourists ran out with the zoo's hours of operation. Grasping at straws though I was, it held as an excuse to face the day and stay my course.

Part Four

Master Painters Association of British Columbia

Quick Tips for a Flawless Do-It-Yourself Painting Experience

Step 4:

Brush, roll or spray your paint onto your surface per the manufacturer's specifications. Do a minimum of two coats of paint. Pay close attention to coverage requirements. Improper application can lead to thinner coats (shortening the life expectancy of the veneer) or thicker coats (compromising the paint's ability to properly stick or dry).

CRADLING A WICKER BASKET OF MY SIZED SMALL washing, I opened my bedroom door to my rebirth. I made the laundry room, stuffed the basin of Layne's throwback washer to the hilt, added powder, examined the rounded, arty numerals on the retro fittings, and pulled back the knob. Unnerved by the monotone *shish* of filling water, the humming of the high-powered heat lamp, and the unanimated slouch of the pot plants, I fled the room with haste.

What's this now? A large individual stood in a pocket of afternoon shadow, hunching over the coffee table, having at Layne's stash. Dressed for burglary in all black, he shuffled through the contents of Layne's cardboard strongbox. But he did so at a methodical clip, one uncharacteristic of thievery, and in the boldness of daytime to boot.

The bandit stood erect to stuff the pockets of his black jeans, displaying a hefty silhouette. He was tall—about an inch shy of Kope—and of a presumably equal weight, although this man was soft and wore his glut at the hips as women do. In the glazy folds of shadow, he appeared an out of shape, out-of-practice ninja. Deploying a smoke bomb, but forgetting step two of two in smoke-bombing: flee.

Surprise may not have held the punch it had two days ago, but fright was still active and I quivered in the kitchen portal like a lit fuse. A creak from the hardwood under my feet compromised my position and the man swiveled his torso to look at me. Time stood still as I prayed he would run.

"Oh, hello. Just getting Layne a smoke. He said Duff-Duff could have one too. You want one? I can ask," said the man. He spoke in the hollow tones of an adult child, one ignorant of the nuances of speech. My guard dropped as swiftly as it had been raised.

"No thanks. Don't smoke."

"You don't smoke? Like, at all?" The stranger could not believe his own ears.

"It's true. I'm Nate. And you are?"

"Me? I'm Duff-Duff. Well, Duffy. I'm Duffy," he struggled with his name and after a minute of measured conversation, I discovered that Duffy was simple. He wouldn't, or couldn't, hurt a flea, and was likely Layne's unofficial gofer. Any loose association with an overweight martial artist slipped away and Duffy now stood more as an effigy of the black free game bowling pin at the St. Thomas Bowling Alley. On Free Game Fridays, if the pinsetter happens to set the black pin in the headpin slot on your lane, you inform the attendant on duty and if you throw a strike, you're awarded a free game voucher. The tickets are idolized at elementary school Show and Tells.

"Where's Layne, Duffy?"

"Out front. Keeping Cyrus from throwing rocks at the dead man in the tree," he said, his affect flat.

"I'm sorry?"

"For what?"

"No. I meant...there's been a death in the trees?" My cheeks flushed at the sound of my own inanity.

"Come see. I found it first," he said proudly.

Wearily I followed Duffy down the stairs, thinking on the way: *What now?* There had been only one homicide in St. Thomas, that I knew of. The accused later said that it was an accident: he was just trying to scare a pesky coon off his property. Everyone sided with him.

I traced Duffy's steps out the front door past Mark's corner unit, across the eskers and fissures of slumping tar, clear of the Pontiac rust-heap, and down and up two curbs. Duffy's upper body appeared to move in different time with his portly southern hemisphere—two sweeps of his arms for each stride of his legs. The black jeans restricted only so much flesh, and each step set into motion whippy pounds that caused his haunches to waddle violently like a dancing dragon at Chinese New Year.

The high temperatures for the week had held steady—prime barbecuing weather for the rooftop guild in Kitschylano. We came to the high chain-link fence on the other side of the street. The fencing hindered access to the massive concrete footholds of the SkyTrain track and the hairy intermittence of trees and brush growing unchecked around them. Intricate murals of graffiti testified to the fence's effectiveness.

We also came upon a short rock-wielding badger-like tramp who answered, only when sternly addressed, to the name Cyrus. Layne was nowhere in sight. Cyrus's face and neck were obscured by an outcropping of copper beard. The bare skin above his cheekbones was olive, but it appeared a good scrubbing would reveal an ivory subfloor. The elastic leg bands on his black cotton B.C. Lions sweatpants were scrunched above his sinewy calf muscles and his white T-shirt was raked with dirt, grass-streaks, and armpit stains (Midday Ochre 844-54). His receding hairline evidenced an age his scatterbrained giddiness sweated to conceal. Frantic with excitement he kicked at the steel links, bouncing on his bare feet as though they were connected to springs. He was acting like a discombobulated monkey. Cyrus registered me as a new face, but he was not the kind to introduce himself.

"Gonna throw again. *Heeheehee.* Hit 'em! *Heeheehee.*" He laughed in hyperventilating gusts, revealing two rotting arches—a brown M where his front teeth had once been intact. (Later I learned from a DJ at one of Dennis's parties that this results from abusing hard drugs a certain way).

The softball sized hunk of asphalt in Cyrus's grimy hands and the pile collected at his bare feet kept my eyes locked firmly on him and out of the trees. I wanted him to launch it. Get that lethal weapon out of his grip. We were tracking what I was led to believe was a cadaver. There was indescribable creepiness in the promise of a dead body closeby but impossible to access. What's the first thing one does at a funeral visitation? Lock eyes with the coffin. But we weren't in the neutral-painted, heavy-aired safety of a funeral home. This was a corpse in the city. Sharing the realm of the living. Not yet officially declared dead. Its family yet to be notified. Body yet to be sponged. Yet to be drained and embalmed. Eyes and mouth yet to be capped and sewn to a closed and locked position. Vain attempts to liven the face with makeup yet to be undertaken. And yet to be brought down from its resting place somewhere in a tree by way of stoning.

Cyrus let fly the speckled rubble with an unsettling grunt, arching it underhand from behind his body like a soldier with a grenade. The sky was a clear blue sheet, backdrop to a flourish of earthen greens and the Sky Way's airborne blacktop. I searched the missile's flight path for a bloated purple face.

The object thudded onto hard, droughty ground in back of a tall sequoia some fifty feet away. A hefty lob for a twittering weasel. I scanned the tree's leafy parasol but saw no trace of disturbed death.

"Can't throw it any gooder than that," said an unruffled Duffy, as though he was an aficionado in the sport of dead man bocce ball.

What? That came close? I thought fervidly. I searched harder until intent found its mark: a strange rock at the base of the sequoia's trunk that wasn't a rock at all, but rather a prostrated lump of men's clothing. In Duffy's world, a dead body nestling in the overland roots at the base of a tree is essentially 'in the tree'.

The body's head and feet were anticlimactically hidden by thick root and wild grass. A tawny vintage suit connected the two invisible dead ends. I was grateful for the fencing, keeping us at fifty feet of clearance with no option but to respect the defenseless thing.

Layne's emergence on the scene detracted me from my mortal reverie.

"Hey Nate pal! Sleep well bud?"

Layne was interrupted by sounds from Cyrus, who now began dispatching his entire ration of projectiles into the field.

"CYRUS! What the fuck did I say? No throwing rocks!" He stepped towards Cyrus posturing to strike, and Cyrus backed away like a frightened animal. "Don't you know it is illegal to tamper with evidence? You could go to jail for that, you crackerjack."

Dying to show off, Layne quickly took charge. "I dialed nine-one-one from the store payphone, let them know the location of the stiff, barriers to entry and whether I seen any suspicious characters of note in the vicinity," he reported. The situation was nirvana for a control freak like Layne. He continued his briefing with proud arms on his hips in a Superman pose. "The cops will be here any second to bag and tag and do forensics, so we must cordon off the crime scene."

This security fence should do the trick, you twit, I thought silently.

"Duffy, I'll take that ciggy now?" said Layne, calling on his personal assistant with a finger snap. From his jean pocket Duffy pinched a decapitated filter and streamers of tobacco strand. "Jesus Christ Duff-Duff! Run your fat ass back up there and get me a *whole* one. Told the cops I'd stick around to direct traffic and I sure as hell can't leave this freakazoid out of my sight." He continued softer: "You understand Duff-Duff, don't you pal?"

"Sorry Layne. Be right back." Duffy woke the Chinese dragon to fetch another smoke for his boss.

Layne clearly owned Duffy. Took advantage of his stumbling-block brain, synonymized his name with 'dumb-dumb', and let him think it was a term of endearment from a friend. He even let Duffy apply the term to himself, proudly. *Said Duff-Duff could have one too,* Duffy had told me upstairs. I gave Layne a disgusted look, but he read my intention wrong.

"Don't get the impression," Layne said, pointing the way of the deceased, "that this is an everyday thing around these parts. This happens everywhere in this city. My hunch, that man out there changed into his Sunday best and came to this field to die with dignity under a warm sun."

"Whatever you say Layne-Layne." It was a subtle, padded

body shot, but my best effort.

Then I simply walked away.

"Righty then. So I'll see you back up at the house bud," said Layne to my back. He said it as though we lived alone on a private acreage of ranchland outside the city limits, safe from harm's way; a hideaway for best buds.

I felt like the ponies at town fairs, strapped into place with blinders on their sunken heads, made to go around in circles for the amusement of others. Yet I was done excusing this good-for-nothing grifter. Layne was a wavering scumbag, cancer veteran or not. I felt pangs of both relief and despair as I finally swallowed this humiliating horse pill of reality. My run-in with death reverted me back to a warming symbol of life: I planned to go inside and call my mother.

With Layne tabulated—irrevocably this time—into my bad books, his building took on an unharnessed shabbiness. Graffiti on the far end units, sun-bleached garbage strewed around its grounds in such frequency it seemed intentional rather than inconsiderate; rusted pipes protruding from the walls like broken bones, a skin of grime on the outer face, all stood at attention.

Just another piece of grime was the woman I now saw. From the middle of the parking lot until our door, I was steeped in the unexpected sight of her: clearly an exhibition some men paid family money to own for a time.

DIFFICULT TO TELL WHICH HEAP OF RUIN WAS HOLDING

the other up. The woman was a bedraggled Mrs. Holme, according to Layne our resident schoolmarm. She was seated in the birthing position, her back against her front door, feet flat on the concrete and knees bent at square angles. The Looney Toons T-shirt she'd donned was too small for a nightgown and stopped short above scabby knees.

Preoccupied with death, had I missed her on my way out? I couldn't see how. The hair on her legs was long and in areas underneath it there was deep bruising—mounting circlets of black-purple-blue like archery targets. Her hair was a frazzled mess and her sallow face—faded magenta lips chapped to splitting, white paste in the corners of her open mouth, and vacant eyes—frightened me.

Her eyes faced the rich indigo sky, but she was in no mind to embrace wonder, let alone colour. She sucked in hard, quick breaths as though attempting to inhale a soul. This was how I envisioned the dead man in the tree to look, except for her sagging breasts under the nightgown. And the wreath of her unshorn salt-and-pepper pubic hair—which showed, nappy around a coral seeing-eye vagina.

In the driest of ironies, the gown that Mrs. Holme had opted for this day was a gag T-shirt with an antagonistic Daffy Duck raising one of his middle feathers on his left wing. Underneath Daffy a caption read **Go Duck Yourself!** In all likelihood, somewhere else in the city at that moment, on a radio station my work van does not receive, some animated DJ was encouraging listeners to put on their tank tops and get outside to bask in a patch of April's warm, anomalous gift.

My legs worked on their own to get me away. My heart ate more of itself. Duffy passed me on the narrow stairwell. The jellied overhang of his midsection peeking out the bottom of his shirt slicked my forearm hair. After he'd passed his path of body odour scented my upward escape route, but I breathed him in unbothered. Nothing more occurred to me. I stood on a square of parquet floor at the top of the stairs and muttered "Think Nate, think," in a clean white panic, over and over again. Blocks of minutes ticked away unaffected. Layne's bedroom door was ajar, creaking as it yawned to subtle gusts from his bedroom window, and it became my bucket of cold water. Layne had always been so careful, but the call to duty outside seemed to have rushed him and he'd forgotten to lock it. My independent will carried me around the unlatched door before the decision had come from my brain, and I hurried about the business of spying.

Smell did not sculpt my impression of the room—I had caught and held my breath in panic like a would-be fireman going naked into a burning building. In any case, the dirty clothes spread on the floor would be redolent of vinegar, my olfactory memory told me; I didn't need a refresher. Light dribbled in from a window whose Venetian blinds were thick with dust and offered a striped view of the rear balcony. This room acted as landfill for the rest of the apartment: an uprooted plant wilting on top of a broken chair that matched his dining set, a corona of speckled topsoil around its green plastic planter; lying in the corner, a gothic black and white portrait of a little girl. A dresser humped the north wall, its surface covered: orange prescription bottles, empty cigarette packs, a lighter, a rubber glove, dirty cutlery (mostly spoons), loose change, and a slew of overflowing tin ashtrays of the variety that sat beside glass sugar silos in The Meat Wagon before the urban smoking ban. Two night tables, equally cluttered, and a slumping unmade queen bed beetled from the south wall.

I skimmed the room once with wide eyes. Anxious about being caught, I tried to pin accurate values on miscellany. The urgency of my spying made it slapdash and mostly forgettable. Mostly. Just off the room's entrance, I could see that Layne's en suite bathroom was a science experiment of mold and mildew. Its garbage bin overflowed like agitated homebrew. White splatters on the square mirror above the sink; my red perspiring face staring back to me.

But I did notice the garbage bin's contents.

Light-headed and with stale air burning my lungs, I fled the bedroom incapacitated, the victim of a house fire watching his microcosm of security implode and char around him. I found the couch and sat disoriented.

Despite what I'd been told of the child Tommy's sleepover, Layne hadn't fitted his bedroom with a recliner and there were used prophylactics in the bathroom garbage.

LAYNE AND DUFFY HAD REAPPEARED. "THOSE PIGS don't know their asses from holes in the ground." Layne griped. Duffy giggled at the swear word, which Layne took as encouragement for another curse. "Fucking faggots." Again Duffy sniggered, but Layne was upset. The police had excused him.

I imagined he had reported his findings and volunteered his citizenly services, and the cops had banished him like they would a pestering child. Possibly with an officious slogan. "We'll take it from here". There was joy to be relished in any undermining of Layne, but I had been inconsolably dazed since coming to a rest on the couch. Staring at the black blob that was my reflection in the TV screen, the smear of Duffy's buttery perspiration still going unnoticed on my arm, I sat alone in shock.

"These feel thin. Are they one-paper? They are. What did I say? Two papers each! Re-roll the fucking joints now, please. And this time, count them out," Layne carped, raising a Zig-Zag rolling paper in each hand. "One Two. One Two. Like you say to yourself when you walk around."

Duffy broke apart his mistakes and started again. He and Layne were preparing joints out of dried pot laid out on two plastic cutting boards. Layne shredded and spun and licked with an illusionist's skill, and before long, a log pile of white cocoons had materialized on the table.

"Imagine a home grower submitting one-paper weak-ass spliffs for pre-rolls. The girls at the Club would carve me good," Layne said to himself. "Pretty quiet back there pal," he prodded me.

It felt as though Layne was speaking into the peep-hole of a prison cell.

"Called the Duff-Duff over to hash out plans for our next big grow," he flapped on. "Bad news though bud. Spider mites went to town on our plants. Pesky shits had a field day. The buds I rescued I'll need to squirrel away for personal. Which means..." he paused. "It means we need to grow more and I got to thinking: why not a lot more. What say you, me, and Duff-Duff here invest in some better grow equipment? Lamps, clones, beds and so on? All in, we're only looking at three grand thereabouts," Layne said to me, wrapping his arm around Duffy's shoulders like one would a kid brother. "Duff's cousin Duke has the connections to unload by the pound. He's a hard-nosed bugger and has blanket protection with the Hell's Angels. Duke loves the Duff-Duff and wants to help him with a quick score. It's foolproof."

In the nebulous reflection of the TV, I saw Layne's hand move up to rub his moustache in the way I once thought wistful.

Safe in my bedroom asylum I once again considered calling home but found I was too jarred. My mother's honed maternal instincts could pick up the subtlest undertones of despair in my voice. She'd ask the questions that I was dying to answer; it would have been insensitive to drop this on her from so far away. I'd worry her sleepless. But boy, did I ever want to hear that manicured milk and honey telephone voice and escape to the simpler facets of life in St. Thomas. Neighbours neglecting their lawns, the new priest at the church and his long-winded sermons, so and so having another baby, the reliable topic of unreliable weather. My mother, a hobby collector of obituaries, would also lay on me the latest St. Thomas obits—"Did you ever meet Mildred Cassidy? She was in your Aunt Yvette's year at St. Joseph's? Well, she was Mildred McCoubrey back then. No? Ran the turkey raffle for years? Well, her stepdad Ron Buchanan is a member out at Union and a man in his Sunday foursome, Dave Maxwell, died suddenly of a heart attack. I didn't know Dave all that well but your father and I went up to Sifton's and lit a candle for the poor man."

I could also expect the update on my not-so-little brother, now a teenager in high school. Mom would tell me what she knew about his life, which was more than the average mother knows of her fifteen-year-old son. They were tightly knit; but the other reason was that unlike the teenagers of my day who drank underage and snuck past their parents' room late at night, Matthew preferred to skip flimflammery, go directly into Ivan and Louise's bedroom, lie at their feet, and candidly reflect on his night or on life in general. Mom would first glean what he drank, where he drank it, in what quantity, and how he'd arrived home; then, happy to have Matthew safe in the nest, she'd let him route their chat at will. The eternal parental problem of casual underage drinking had been devalued by the health struggles Matthew had had to endure. Life was too short to worry about cliché misbehavior or obligatory battle lines.

Matthew was not as forthcoming with me. When forced to 'come and talk to your brother on the phone', he would concede one-word answers and pose no questions. This from a boy who once worshipped the ground I walked on and loved nothing more than playing mini-stick hockey in the basement with his ultra cool hero. Mom would console me by saying he was in a transition that everyone experiences, but I couldn't help thinking that underneath everything Matthew resented me for abandoning him for Vancouver during his developmental years —a time laden with confusion. And maybe even deeper down, in the raw, irrepressible abyss of knee-jerk human emotion, he resented me for my healthy heart and lungs. For the easy time I'd had of childhood while he was in and out of hospital, baby ribcage sawed apart before his first birthday. For having to watch me flounder at sports knowing what his innate athleticism could have done with an intact body—the kind wasted on me.

Too late to call now anyway, I thought. I crushed a pillow into my chest.

The police cruisers and the ambulance decommissioned their streaming lights and soberly dispersed. The sky shaded to black. "Things will look different in the morning," I could hear mom saying as I fell asleep.

THE PNEUMATIC ROAR OF A COMMERCIAL JET, LIKE A thousand gorging buzz-saws, invaded my bedroom and spring-boarded me from sleep. I jerked the cord beside the window over my bed, sending the thin metal slats bunching upward. There it was, in the black wing of night, below even the low-lying fog: a Boeing 737-800 in distress and locked in a nosedive.

The red-eye from Toronto had circled out over the Pacific in preparation for its approach into Vancouver International and had encountered a thick sea fog, causing it to bend off course. The pilots had overshot the airport, and in the confusion, lost control of their craft. Though the plane was flying a line straight for our building, I knew by its trajectory that the crash site would be well in advance of us. I imagined the panic on board as the eleven inflight crew members prepared their ninety-eight passengers, some children, for an Emergency Landing even as the plane was about to crash. I knew all of this just by looking out the window, but I didn't question how.

SSSSSSSS...BOOM!!!

The deafening explosion hit blocks north of Broadway Street and turned night into day. Mistaking impact for a contained incident (the downed airliner skidding to a quick stop like an Ultimate Frisbee on grass). I cowered as the now churning fireball of debris bulldozed a path towards me. The ear-splitting thunder of destruction and *whoosh* of consumed oxygen built as the wreckage careened across the thirty-foot-deep railroad trench, toppled the SkyTrain's concrete supports—incinerating the dead man's sequoia and surrounding grove and devouring the security fence—and cut a gash in Grandview Highway North like a Ginsu knife cutting through a pop can. One tenth of a second left in my existence. *Time for one last thought.* I finally thought.

The whiny grumble of a Cessna plane, like two idling chainsaws, tickled my bedroom air, gradually nudging me from sleep. *Was it a dream, or an overindulgent premonition?* I jerked the cord beside the window over my bed, sending the thin metal slats bunching upward. There they were, in the black wing of night, below the low-lying fog: a line of transport trucks heading south on Grandview Highway North. Unlike most rigs the cabs and freight boxes on these eighteen-wheelers were polished to a prominent shine, each with detailed pictures advertising their cargo: Bridgestone Tire, Lola Chassis, Ethanol Fuels, Holmatro Rescue Equipment, Motorola Racing, Team KOOL Green. *Hunh?*

After a day of dismantling, the Indy circus was getting an early five a.m. jump out of town and using my quiet road to do so.

Never more relieved to be on the front end of a workweek, I soaked up some pre-office time sponging yolk from a runny egg in a coffee shop near the plant that wheedled most of its profits as a cigarette stop for nearby factory workers. Then I sat on Briscoll Inc.'s cold steps, waiting for the first of the key-yielding head honchos to purr into the parking lot in his luxury sedan and mistake my punctuality for rededication to the company's mission statement. Both us would ignore that this was two sentences hammered-out over neat scotch.

Once inside I sipped tea in the showroom and watched the pre-shift cleaning crew perform. They proceeded with the choreography of circus tumblers, and the sight made me reminisce about my days when I was first hired at Briscoll Inc.: arriving before the cleaners every morning, fireworks in my eyes.

Now, moving at a furious clip, against the backbeat of an internal clock the shortest of the cleaners went for his mop bucket and swabbed himself into a dry corner.

Layne had to have dressed that broken woman in respectable clothing and warned her to keep her mouth shut.

How? By offering her drug money? Threatening her?

These types of hardy reminders blew in hastily, like prairie weather, throughout my long day.

After three coworkers had inquired into my health I examined my face in the men's room mirror. The smell of dry urine and gritty orange industrial soap hung in the single stall lavatory. A drab place for self-analysis. I prodded at my tired mug, noting the beginnings of permanent bags under my eyes. Not unlike the cockles under the eyes of my manager Bert, or the dunes under the eyes of his manager Ed.

My first day in the building, Bert had underscored **Accelerated Growth** as a selling feature of my new position. He had over-delivered on half his promise. Two years had now blown past like a nameless comet, and only a faint beam of oddball memories remained.

Layne has $1250 of yours in his possession. You paid him in cash, remember. There is no marijuana left to innocently sell off to friends.

Instead, Layne asks more cash of you to traffic a chargeable-offense load of pot via the notoriously barbaric Hell's Angels.

You will retire a bald paint salesman, a mediocre one at that, having never set foot on Australian soil.

I ate lunch in the hot sunshine, out at the picnic table with Bill. Catching wind of the day's juicy gossip on the office grapevine, I felt for my friend: he was also having a banner day.

"Ro-ro-ro-he knows I don't have my lift lice-lice-lice-lice-ticket," Bill said over his bologna and cheese on white.

With the plant down one of its two forklift drivers due to illness,

Ron Thompson, working with a skeleton crew and under the gun to get an overdue order on the road, had reluctantly assigned Bill to lift truck #2. One hour had passed before Bill panicked with the sticky gearshift, hit the gas and rammed the long metal teeth of the seven thousand pound automaton into the support beams of some scaffolding shelving product forty feet up. It was from that height that four five-gallon pails of coating—weighing fifty pounds apiece—had plummeted. Three had exploded safely on the warehouse floor, sending shoots of red glop along the concrete. The fourth had fallen directly onto the cockpit, striking the protective metal slat above Bill's head. The reverberation had deafened him temporarily. The thin roof plate had dented but held true, preventing Bill's head from becoming porridge. Bill had sat motionless, a square waterfall of red paint oozing down around his seat: a scene straight out of a horror movie. Alerted by the brassy clash Ron Thompson had raced around the corner and practically fallen to his knees. For the briefest of moments Ron thought Bill had finally gone and done what he had come so close to doing countless times before and what his older brother warned him he might do if he wasn't more careful: killed himself.

The area was cordoned off for safety, making it look more a homicide crime scene after the gore. All but the company brass (whose interest in the accident ran along deeper lines), Ron, and myself, were now having a laugh at Bill's expense. The rigmarole of bosses drafting Bill's walking papers, Ron threatening to quit, and an eventual stalemate, had also been set in motion. It would be a familiar but even pricklier time for Bill. He had begun stuttering his take on the accident.

"Sorry, who said what?" I requested at the inset. I pecked pensively at my vending machine lunch, lost in my own calamity. Attuned to my distraction, the forbearing Bill shelved his problem to hear out mine. "Out with it", he said in his approximating tongue.

Ugly minutiae jetted from my mouth. Layne shooting down my dreams like clay pigeons at a skeet shoot.

"Pull!"...*Crack! Crack!*

"Pull!"...*Crack! Crack!*

Bill reflected quietly on the breadth of occurrence in my life. *All in three days*, his face seemed to say. He advised me not to give Layne the weed money, to be wary of him, to start planning for a move, and other sound, obvious instructions. He took out a pen and wrote his phone number on a strip he tore from his brown lunch bag. He told me I was free to call day or night.

The very last thing he said to me before going inside the warehouse to be gummed by the plant crew was the only phrase I ever heard him say without falter. It seemed to take a terrific amount of concentration. "Nate, bud, I know you are going to win," Bill said. Referring to no challenge in particular: his way of letting me know he had faith in his friend.

I thanked him for the gesture, no further along myself but gladder for having somehow made Bill feel better about his own quandary.

You continually sanitize Tommy out of your Layne recall. You haven't forgotten though, have you? Layne desecrated him that first night. Said the boy slept on his recliner when Layne never owned one in the first place. You do remember leaving Tommy there alone?

At five-thirty Bert strutted into my office to remind me of my dreaded QPE: my Quarterly Performance Evaluation. 'Cupie' for short. It was scheduled for the following day.

I occupied one of the windowless inner offices in the building. Hung next to a large whiteboard was the 2001 calendar our pigment supplier had dropped off with one of our orders; each month featured an "action shot" from their manufacturing facility in Bellingham, Washington, and my favourite was February: two men in lab coats and latex gloves examining a beaker of pigment, one contemplatively scratching the sides of his chin while the other wrote on a clipboard. It begged the question *What are you two mad scientists concocting? Super Pigment?* The rest of the office was bare paint (Badlands 666-16); now Bert stared at me, combing his moustache with his fingers, like I was a beaker of pigment.

"You hear the latest on Spilliam?" Bert grunted.

"Yes. And blame should fall squarely on Ron. He put him in

that seat without the required training and hours."

"I don't know. Ron wasn't the one who rammed the shelving. I mean shi-i-i-i-it." He sniggled like an idiot. "Leave it to old Spillzy to get the job done. Am I right?"

I didn't answer him.

"No offense, but you look like a bag of shit today. What gives?"

"Thought I rented on a nice, quiet street. Woke up to an army of semis this morning."

"Wait, where did you say you moved?"

"Grandview Highway North, between Clark and Commercial." I sighed, kneading my forehead.

"Well, there you go," Bert said with a wave of his hand. "Truckers use Grandview to bypass the morning rush on the number one. You live on Downshift Alley."

"It has a name?"

"Well it *is* a well-known shortcut. Near the SkyTrain line, right? Bit dumpy, am I right?"

"Right! Yes! We discussed it three weeks ago. Remember? I asked if the area was a safe bet. You didn't say boo."

What had I done to get thrown into the fish bowl with this blowfish? I asked the Fates.

Layne told you he was a master chef. Instead he bullied the homeless, bullied Duffy, screamed at Kope (and meddled with his luggage), gawked at you in your underwear, hit the roof at The Meat Wagon, lied about Mark and Mrs. Holme, about his parents, about the weed, about the cable, about the traffic. Is rageful, delusional and perverted. And a dead body was found yesterday, fifty yards from your pillow.

It's six o'clock; nearly time for home.

THE EARLY VIEWING OF *THE LORD OF THE RINGS: THE Fellowship of the Ring* let out in a darkness lit by the yellow flicker of marquee bulbs. Dennis would have had a thing or two to say about me taking in a film puffed with so much hype—and during its debut week no less. My mouth felt desiccated from salty popcorn and my butt was numb from hours on a cheap theatre seat. I unlocked my bike from the rack, clicked the chin strap to my mushroom cap helmet, tucked my pant legs into my socks, and descended to Grandview Highway North.

The snap decision to see the movie had resulted from a failure to devise an airtight exit strategy from Layne. Also from a billboard; an ad on the side of a bus; two consecutive bus stop posters; and a front-page feature in the window of a newspaper dispenser. But flip-flopping from fantasy to my awaiting reality and not having read Tolkien, I'd laboured to follow the plotlines. The epic had served a different and greater purpose: over three hours Layne-free. The other kickback was that I had happened upon Cheap Tuesday. Extra titillation for my pennywise ways.

Weaving around parked cars I glided from Clark Road onto Grandview Highway North and jogged on my bike pedals along the roadside with the security fence. Another tepid T-shirt night, but the cooling draft of my motion goose-pimpled the exposed skin at my neck and forearms. At this end of Grandview, the streetlights were erected sparingly and to an outsider I was vanishing and rematerializing in slants of contributive light and annulling dark that marked the route back to Layne.

Not a solitary light was on outside our complex, the spinning head asleep as I approached, breaching shadowy reminders of my freefall. The tree in the waste lot. Mrs. Holme's front door. The hallway to the garbage closet. The banquet table for the homeless. The vibratory *hummmm* of the pot nursery generator. The couch where I slept under Layne's watchful eye. His unlocked bedroom door.

For my safe passage Layne had left on the hallway lighting— two bulbs (one burnt out), and a retro dome fixture. A dead housefly in the hull of the shade and a flossy settling of dust limited the good bulb's wattage. Once, I'd looked for the switch with no success. Secretively wired to a toggle in the hallway closet? It would have to be irresponsibly left on the entire night, and what hell would there be to pay?

A folded piece of lined yellow paper, slipped under my bedroom door waited to serve its notice. Using both blue and red pen Layne had written in his sloppy illiterate hand:

Nate,

Con-sid-er-ate [kuhn-sid-er-it]
-adjective
1. showing kindly awareness or regard for another's feelings, circumstances, etc.:
i.e. A very considerate critic.

Scripting next to an open dictionary, he had continued on with a misspelled advisory on the merits of informing him when I will be absent for dinner, ending with the postscript:

P.S. Don't worrie about it buddy. We'll get it rite.
Your pal,
Layne

AT THE HUB OF OUR HUMID ONTARIO SUMMERS, roosts of black bats would commingle in the canopy of a shady maple on our street. As a child, when the moon was fat and luminous I would sit on the front verandah and watch them plunge down above evening strollers. The winged vermin would seem to dive-bomb the people, pulling up inches short of their heads, and then stealthily swooping back to their towering vantages.

For my year-end science project in grade three, I had chosen to research the bats. I'd learned from the World Book Encyclopedia that bats play an important role in the ecosystem by pollinating trees and flowers and eating the bugs that spread disease and raze crops. I had particularly enjoyed discovering that they like the taste of mosquitoes most. I also knew they were blind and used sonar to navigate.

"Three bats just flew past your head you know," I'd say to passing neighbours or to friends coming over for sleep-overs.

"Oh God! No way!" they'd shriek, frantically rubbing their quivering hands through their hair. And I'd laugh with the high-pitched squeak of the bats, smug in my knowledge that bats don't attack people's hair.

It was as wholesome an upbringing as they come. My

brother, two sisters, and I had a Christmas morning tradition. It was the duty of the first to wake to round up the others on the shampooed trapezoid-shaped rose carpeting that separated our bedroom doors. The four of us would then form a sleepy-eyed human train along the banister at the top of the stairs. Ranged from youngest to oldest (this made Margaret the lead car before Matthew came along), with hands on the shoulders of the sibling in front, we'd chug down the stairs making *choo-choo* noises until we'd reached the train yard of gifts and treats in our family room. The air breathed safety and warmth. The Christmas Train is one of endless examples of my sheltered childhood where love, affection and sugar cereal were never in short supply. Major atrocities eluded our family for some unknown cosmic reason. Terrible fates— destitution, terminal illnesses, criminal convictions, amputations, suicides—were dealt to others in our township. Lightning would strike down all around us, but the six Mills on Forest Avenue always continued unscathed.

My awareness of our charmed fates had developed at an early age. Why us? Why were we provided the map to the mine field? In the moments before sleep kidnapped me I would look sheepishly past the reflection of my Popeye nightlight on my bedroom window, convinced that Jesus's head was floating outside (only the head for some reason), and timidly scan the black pane for an outline of His face. I imagined His eyes following me throughout the day too, in the knotholes on my school desk, in the trapped air bubbles under icy sidewalks, in the shallow waters rolling over local riverbed rock. It had comforted me knowing that He'd been there to make sure Mommy would never burn alive in a mangled car, Daddy would never go postal at work and blast a tunnel through his boss.

Tragedy had in fact touched our family, but in those earlier times my youth spared me the pain of awareness. I remember mom bringing me to see Grandpa Ben who had been dying of cancer. A decorated war hero who'd earned the Victoria Cross for valour by shooting down Hitler's Nazis in his Spitfire, he lay cut down by microorganisms. I loosely remember following with my fingers the maze of metal support bars on his hospital bed and eating round English mints from a crystal dish Grandma had brought in special for Grandpa's visitors, but that's all. Then one day we simply stopped going to St. Thomas Elgin General to visit Grandpa Ben.

One time, I'd thought our clean streak had ended. It was a wintry February evening; I was ten; my baby teeth had been replaced by a mash of crooked fangs much too large for my mouth. I was frantically pacing the slippery tiles on my Grandma Agnes's kitchen floor (she cleaned more often after Grandpa Ben's passing). My mother had entered the hospital seven hours earlier, and we'd had no word of her progress.

At last news arrived: of a new baby brother.

He had mercifully evened out the boy/girl ratio in our house at a perfect three to three. Mom was healthy. We'd celebrated joyously, as a family free from tragedy often has cause to do.

Shortly after my parents named him Matthew Joseph, the doctors discovered a congenital heart defect known as Truncus Arteriosis. His aorta and left pulmonary artery had not detached in the first eight weeks of pregnancy and oxygen-poor blood from his body was polluting the oxygen-rich blood from his lungs. It appeared that our unsinkable ship of providence, that had bypassed every storm, had been battered off course and run aground. And the comeuppance for years of dumb luck had landed heavily upon one innocent unborn heart.

Open heart surgeries at six and eighteen months had left a zipper scar on Matthew's chest, a mark more often found on wrinkled skin. Most of his early baby pictures showed him attached to tubes and machinery, his prognosis Touch-and-Go. For lack of space in the house, Matthew had slept in my room. Each night before bed I would check his breathing and his heartbeat. The seconds before seeing his tiny chest rise up had been a nightly torture. With my hand on his heart I'd kiss his soft cheek goodnight—the petite bone nestling squarely between my lips—and beg Jesus for my brother's recovery.

Years passed and Matthew's cheekbones outgrew my lips. The double bed and crib were taken out of our room and replaced by matching singles. Matthew strengthened and through routine checkups his team of specialists had grown evermore optimistic.

One night in high school I'd snuck into the house late, drunk from a party, and splashed into bed fully-clothed.

"Nate," Matthew had whispered from his twin, a boy of four who'd huffed more anesthetic than most do in a lifetime.

"What are you doing up this late, hunh bud?" I'd called back, trying my best to right my slurs.

"You didn't check me tonight."

My layman's medical checkups had been covert, or so I'd thought. But Matthew had known. I had no idea for how long, but he had.

"We have early mass tomorrow. Didn't want to wake you. Now go to sleep, bud."

"OK."

A few minutes had passed.

"Nate?"

"Yeah Matt?"

"I know where I wanna work when I grow up." Matthew had been hashing out future plans into the night and now couldn't sleep.

A wide smile, shrouded in darkness, lit my face. "You do," I'd said, trying to match my tone with the seriousness he'd obviously put into his decision. "Can you tell me, or is it a secret?"

"Yes, I can…I mean…no, it's not a…you wanna know?"

"You bet Matt, but then we sleep, OK?"

"OK. It's McDonald's!"

"McDonald's? Why there bud?" Thinking: *No brother of mine!*

"The smell."

The smell.

That tender moment and a boatload of others had shored up a blind faith in me; a restful assurance in the fate of my family. Years later we were all at a rented lakeside cottage, hungry from the beach and readying to feast on a spread of cold salads, cheeses and deli meats, when my mother had received a call: the Bourdeau's youngest, Jonah, had succumbed to meningitis in the night. My older sister and I were in high school with his older siblings at the time. Jonah was only six years old, the same age as

Matthew.

"That poor family," Mom had said with a quiver. "When you see those kids in school, you tell them how sorry you are for their loss." She'd looked at each of us in turn. Our faces darkened from sun, teeth white in contrast: a happy olden day minstrel show. "Be thankful for everything you have in this life. That could easily have been us."

She hadn't sounded convinced and neither were us kids.

Like my personal sense of the neighbourhood bats, we believed we were not to be targeted.

PASSING TRANSPORT TRAILERS ALERTED ME TO

daybreak once again. This time it was a mangy lineup compared to the sleek and colourful motorcade of Indy. Standard makes and models; noisier undercarriages; body and chrome cowled by a hide of road grime—Vancouver truckers were unaccustomed to washing their trucks regularly in winter or spring. Minimal one-colour decals on the boxes, shoddy out-of-shape drivers getting a later start than yesterday's crew. Awakened by *them*? I thought foolishly that this was worse than Indy's rude awakening the morning prior. Then I realized I was losing it.

Lying in bed, listening to the crank of tight gears and the whine of loose brakes and working up the energy to alleviate the pressing in my bladder, I heard the squawk of locking tires out front. I looked out the window to see two imposing men piling out of a black van, baseball bats in hand. I lost sight of them when they stepped under my rotted balcony, though it was soon clear where they were headed. Our door hurtled open and four heavy boots were tramping their way up our flight of stairs.

Oh my God! They are in our apartment! Oh God no!

Trembling terror.

Clambering for a weapon, quaking and weak, clad in only my underwear, I lamented deliriously that I had grabbed the worst

219

possible club from my golf bag: I had not hit a clean four-iron in years. In the corner where my bed abutted the two walls I squatted above my pillow on my hind limbs like a stone gargoyle, frozen with fear, the four-iron gripped tightly in my stronger hand. *Could I strike a man? Do I have that in me? Call out to them? Look for a gun first? Get behind the door? Jump them straight away? Swing wildly? Oh God! Why am I here? You're about to wish you were dead!*

Watching my closed bedroom door intently from the far corner of my bed, I focused on the outlying noises. Seconds prolonged as they drew nearer my safe haven. I could no longer think. I lost control of my body and urine soaked through my white cotton. Somewhere in the apartment a door ripped open. Its tremour echoed from the vicinity of my closet, as though they were entering my bedroom through a trap door in the bathroom. Without budging I jumped out of my skin. There came the mumbles of three people—two deep, one high and pleading—as if in my room, but not in my room. *Am I out-of-body? Are they in here and I'm not?*

Wait, listen, they're next door.

Through the paper-thin wall I heard the voices in counterpart alternating stern demands and defensive pleas, but I could not make out the words. I dared not breathe or budge an inch, though my sodden briefs had chilled and were making my crotch itch. The hostility next door dilated fully when the hoarser of the two began to pummel the pleading one. I distinctly recall the rhythm of thuds. With the timed ease of a repetitive-motion chore they battered this nameless, faceless person with the one-two consecutive hammering of men pounding railway ties into place. The sandwiching of moans between blows scored, then disemboweled, my conscience.

Then I heard the men retrace their steps to the idling van. Their pace was halcyonic, leisurely even. *Had they gotten the wrong apartment? Is it Duffy's cousin and the Hell's Angels? Are they after Layne's weed?* I was a tottering ruin.

Shamefaced at my pussyfooting and for the lapse of motor skills in not dialing 9-1-1., I decompressed sufficiently to turn to the window and crimp the blind. I wanted to recoup a shred of dignity by spying out their license plate number. I caught one glance as the van drifted past the Pontiac 6000 and turned out of our lot towards downtown. **866 LYS**. Myopic truckers meanwhile, concerned only with points A and B, drove their clamorous rigs up Downshift Alley as the sun crowned the horizon in their mirrors.

I slouched back onto a dry plot of bed, wondering what society expected of a person in my position. The crotch itching persisted, so I changed my spoiled briefs for pyjama pants and a T-shirt and put my ear to the wall: not a peep. I paced my room torridly. I tried visualizing the license plate number again, but was too wrung out to put the six characters into memory. Unable to think, I set down the golf club and unclenched my stiff white hand, willing the blood back. I overheard Layne leave his bedroom and begin mucking about our common room.

I ran to him.

"Whoa Nate," Layne said calmly. "My friend, you're shaking." He added this whimsically, as if soothing a trotter pony kicking up a little fuss.

Hysterically out of control, I launched into a four-day backlog of kaleidoscopic rage, fear, and dread. Jaw clenched and breathing heavily through bared teeth, I snarled sentence fragments, fanatical with the rock-bottom abandon that follows wetting yourself with cowardice years into manhood. "Listen to me!" I yelled. "This guy. Right next door. Maybe dead. I don't know. Do something!"

"Where? That side?" Layne pointed with a hitchhiker thumb, still smiling. I concurred with vigorous nodding. "Ah, that's Ol' Cory's pad. You're just buggin' amigo." His brush-off made me snap. I pushed Layne backwards, nearly knocking him flat. Balance retrieved and face now cast in a cringing, pouty mask, Layne relented. "Fine then. Christ. I'll check in on him." He traversed the long way to the stairwell, around the couch out of arms' reach. On the first step down the stairs he spoke. "My friend, you had what they call a nightmare. It happens."

This condescending prod rekindled my fire. Fed up with being Layne's prison tail, I bawled him out as he left for Ol' Cory's flat and the police work denied him a day ago. "Shut your damn mouth! I was in your room Layne. I know everything. Everything you've been hiding. You, you—you *fraud*!"

Having validly passed the call to action over to its rightful owner, I made myself presentable for work. A headlong grooming sweep, straightjacketed in reflection.

Layne knows the guy, he can deal with it. Imagine two dead in two days. Probably drug-related. User ripping off dealer. Dealer ripping off supplier. Supplier ripping off drug lord. The underbelly of society, slithering around your front step!

Mere moments from escaping on my bicycle, Layne strutted in with a saccharine smile on his thin lips and a canary in his belly. *I know something you don't know*, the patronizing face sang. "Ol' Cory says he'll go halfsies with you on a Ritalin program if you eighty-six the yelling."

"What?"

"He's in there right now having his loose-leaf breakfast. Ol' Cory is old school. Rolls his own tobacco. Calls it tabacki. Funny old coot."

"Upstairs on this side?" I challenged.

"Yeppers."

"Impossible. You're lying."

"C'mon my friend. It has been a topsy-turvy kind of weekend. Well, hasn't it? Look, I know. I'm dog-tired too. But your Cory Story, I mean, that was something else."

"Why should I believe *anything* you say? I'm no idiot. I heard them. I *saw* them." *I pissed myself because of them!*

I juggled with the idea of slipping his cotton belt out of its loops and strangling him until his dippy face assumed the purple of his robe.

Layne packed down his smile and in the bipolarity that was his gift, he began groveling in a glumness near to tears. "Oh God. I'm so sorry," he blubbered.

It was all too much. I made a motion to leave, but Layne took desperate hold of my handlebar. "No, please," he begged.

"*I* work, and I don't want to be late." I long suspected he didn't work as a landscaper. Layne a manual labourer? He couldn't raise a shovel without a jack.

"All I ask for is five minutes. Please Nate. I can explain everything," Layne wept now, plea-bargaining for redemption.

I agreed sorely, equal parts scared, and curious over what his admission might be. Layne requested we go to the balcony: "It's, like, another celebration out there, buddy," which meant he was roped in a nicotine fit. Standing alone on the back porch, waiting for a nervous Layne to retrieve a pack of cigarettes from his bedroom, I discovered that the heat wave was persevering. I put the renegade temperature in the area of nineteen insistent degrees—sweltering for an April sunup anywhere in Canada, but especially rare in temperate Vancouver. Mirthlessly I eyed the big trees, missing my St. Thomas home. My scattered brain then flipped to the next balcony over and Layne's leery report on 'Ol' Cory'. I went so far as to question whether or not Layne faked looking, possibly waiting outside our front door for ten buffer minutes. Had I even heard him on the adjacent stairs? Could there be a beggarded bloody heap in there with my name on it? By not acting, had I consented to its misery? Its paralyzing? Its murder? Out came Layne with hands full—lit cig in the right, a three-high stack of books in the left. Ordinarily the lighting of his smoke inside would have gotten to me. I guess the sole advantage of major setbacks is that minor annoyances lose their heft. Layne shelved the books between his hand and pelvic bone and stood still. "OK Layne, off like a band-aid," he pepped himself, exhaling. He looked revitalized. I was in that acute state of exhaustion where one starts to contemplate gravity and man's ceaseless battle to remain erect until death's sweet release.

"Nate, bud, I'm sorry. You know I'm not in remission. It was bound to crop up. I wanted to be straight with you from the get-go. God, I hate liars. But you would have breezed by without giving this place a second look. You know you would have."

I had thought something about his health history was fishy. He looked sick. He never ate.

He had full-blown cancer.

I was now acutely aware that Layne also had me physically boxed in. The only way off the balcony was through him, or over the railing.

"There's no easy way to say this, so," Layne said, pausing for a long drag. "I have AIDS."

Peculiar sensation: the world grinding to a halt on its axis and the shriek from its brakes ringing out in your eardrums. My craven physiological defense drowned out the finer points of Layne's confession. Sound bites I gathered:

"...I'm no faggot..."

"...it's all in there bud..."

"...sex and needles..."

He bent back his pinky finger for sex and ring finger for *needles*. After four full days of treading water, my nose and mouth finally sank below the waterline and I entered an enforced calm. The three life preserver books, which Layne handed to me to stay afloat, were titled *Living With AIDS, AIDS in the Homestead* and *The Essential AIDS Factbook*. Library books with foggy plastic protecting the jackets, and yellowing pages. Near the end of our Talk, Layne addressed quite simply, matter-of-factly, as though it was an incidental footnote, that he knew I must have seen the drug paraphernalia in his room, and he hinted at resorting to heroin for escape. Then he held up his pledge hand to say he hadn't used since we met, crediting me as his inspiration.

"I'm so sorry. Are we cool? Can we call this a fresh start to a lengthy friendship?" Layne offered his pledge hand and awaited linkup. On April 5, 2001 at seven-fifteen a.m. Pacific Time, a call to truce.

"I'm so sorry Layne. Yeah, we're cool. We'll call it a do-over," I croaked. His skinny hand wrapped around mine like an eel and I considered every open pore and every nick and scrape, fresh or healed, that my right hand had ever incurred. I pictured his blood as blue while my backbone reconfigured to gelatin.

"I should go." I moved forward.

Layne stepped aside. "Yes, of course. The call to corporate arms. There are asses to kick and names to take. Duty calls!"

Layne had originally used his knack for rhetoric to charm me into a lease agreement. I was now a landed fish in the grip of a sadistic fisherman, the barbed lure torn from my guts and dangled playfully in front of my eyes as I gawped for release.

Layne shadowed me inside back to my bike, down the stairs and out the front door, asking questions and offering advice about the day ahead. Once outside, he speed-walked at my side, engaging me like a pilot's wingman, talking himself winded, as far as the street.

There I lost him. I was off and running as though a starter pistol had been shot, busily creating space between him and me.

I can't say how long Layne stood there. Pleased as punch with his zeroing of the scale and drinking in the wag of my fish-tailing bike.

MY LIFE WAS A SPEED-WOBBLE. A SPEED-WOBBLE IS the stitch in time that follows tripping and precedes its fall. It is the ungainly, futile attempt to recover from a loss of balance by whipping one's body into a frenzy of thrashing and flaying. But momentum is directed downward and the body crashes onto the base surface, whether earth, concrete, gymnasium floor or rock bottom. I know the sensation intimately.

Angry and alone, I sat in my sad little office, pounding my keystrokes, losing my place over and over again and being less than princely with callers both internal and external. I didn't have the parts for the grandiose display of job/life weariness that was playing itself out in my head: heaving my computer monitor into the wall like a medicine ball and lighting my pigment calendar on fire. Instead I flicked my dusty-from-underuse stapler labelled NATHAM over the front edge of my desk down to the carpet below, where it landed with a soft thud. If I'd had it in me to go really postal, I knew, I wouldn't have been stuck behind this desk in the first place.

At lunchtime I opted for a long mindless walk in the sooty mechanical plainness of my work hood. And so I was feeling all the more weak and defeated when Domestic Sales Manager Bert Francis arrived for an inopportunely slated QPE with faltering sales representative Nathan Mills, aka Pinnopio, the nickname I was saddled with by the plant crew.

Bert relished the officiousness required of him in these meetings, stepping up his dress a few measures and laying all jokiness aside. Silk-tied Bert entered my office, returned NATHAM to its rightful place and with his game-day air of authority and mineralized stare, called the Cupie to session. "April fifth, two thousand one. Quarter One. Employee Assessment for Nathan Mills, Outside Sales Representative, Coatings Division," he proclaimed, scribbling notes with a special-occasion silver ballpoint and a leather-bound notepad. He shimmied his moustache from side to side as though shooing invisible flies from his cheeks. Out there in the lukewarm bath of human existence Bert was an unsociable, insecure jag-off. But here, in this teeny soap bubble of an office, in a dirty gutter in South Vancouver, he ruled supreme. "On Management's behalf, I'd like to thank you for your past, present, and future efforts in support of this company." Same lead-in for every Cupie. "However, we are experiencing an even greater lag in sales revenue from your department." Outside the door the framed Vanderpost Estates aerial photo hung in veneration on the wall, the legendary big one, The Jerry Special. "Have you been focusing on the Revenue Generator Model I taught you?" Bert probed, ploughing forward. "Filling up the Drum with key decision makers?" All of the graying brown hairs on his peanut head had been treated with Just For Men hair dye and feathered into place with the black comb in his back pocket. "Are you working on the Selling Intangibles list I e-mailed you last month?" His hair had the fluffiness of a brown baby chick. Very Eighties and very distracting. "The problem with ninety-nine-point-nine percent of salesmen is that they do the legwork to a T without even asking for the sale." A draft was lifting the shorter, flightier strands of hair at Bert's crown. "What are you using today? Can we agree to team up on X, Y or Z project today? Shall I write you up a P.O. for the discounted skid quantity of Futura-Coat 8000 today? Close. Close. Close." Anything for a canister of Brylcreem to slick down Bert's flippant hair. "Selling is not a luck/suck gamble. It's a science. My words, your thesis. And I'm going to mentor you to that PhD." Even a pair of scissors would do. Cut the irksome flyaways off at the scalp. "Are you prepared to rededicate yourself and earn your PhD, Nate?"

"Sorry?" I drew my eyes back from the top of his head to his imperious stare.

"Have you been listening to a single word of this?"

"A single word?" I asked searchingly.

"Am I boring you Nate?" Bert was beside himself. His platinum-level sales workshop flattened by stargazing—by the very daydreaming I had warned him of in our first meeting.

I had no choice. Out I came with my Layne Story, up to the minute and down to the last detail, including Tommy but excluding my incontinence.

To be fair, Bert did become my push to action. He suggested I sign out the Briscoll van for the evening and he asked Big Ron Thompson—from whom Bert regretted soliciting any favour, no matter how small—if he had the storage space to temporarily house my gear. When I'd suggested Bert play wingman, he stopped short, citing a soccer practice for his second son from his third marriage. Those ankle-deep in the little league soccer world know that under-eight practices can be grueling, nightlong affairs.

I ended up in a nervous search for a second set of hands, but Dennis was in Europe on business. Outside of Dennis, a help-hide-the-body-and-lie-to-the-police class of friend, I was at a loss for a stand-in. First I asked Kevin, a muscly native of Woodstock, Ontario (an hour's drive from St. Thomas) who worked in Powders with Karl. Kevin's mouth was ringed with hair—a look inexplicably popular amongst many Canadian males. Dennis called it "First Birthday", referring to the child that gorges on chocolate cake in his highchair, leaving a brown disc around his mouth. With our hometown connection and relative closeness in age, Kevin and I got on reasonably well. I thought it devious to ask for Kevin's help without laying out the whole Layne Story for him; his response was positive.

"I'd help. But I'm *not* volunteering to drop in on some psychotic, hombre-shooting, cake-drilling, faggoteer with shit for blood. Sorry. You're a good guy and all, but take your farmer dick between your legs and go fuck yourself," Kevin proclaimed. He and Karl had special ways with words, possibly from huffing cementitious powders forty hours a week, fifty weeks a year.

Having eavesdropped on Kevin's subsequent overexertion of my Layne Story for the boys in the plant, Bill came to offer me help immediately, even though Kevin's made-up bits about the facial boils and bestiality had rocked him. He suggested we keep his overprotective brother out of it. I hadn't considered asking Bill, but was thankful he'd jumped on board.

At four thirty Bill and I met at the work van. Bert was walking to his Toyota Camry. Circling an upside-down fist he halted us at the gate. I dutifully rolled down my window.

"Remember guys: bend at the knees. Saves your backs and your anal virginities. *Chee-chee-chee.* And don't stay past dinner. I hear his favourite board game is Chutes and Ladders. *Chee-chee-chee,*" Bert goaded us by means of a macho outer crust, but I knew that later that evening his jelly-filled insides would be soused in TV Guide listings and a soggy microwave dinner. His sad whisk of a reality seemed my destiny.

The radio scanner spooled past weak signals the entire drive, even past my normally reliable news station. I would have settled for anything—English, French, Chinese—to drown out Bill's nervous picking; he was playing the rolled seam on the seat like a banjo. *Pick. Pick. Pick. Pick. Pick.* As he did so his head kept moving: from me, to the windshield, to the mirror, to me, like a hungover pigeon sussing out food scraps on a pier. When we neared Grandview Highway North Bill couldn't stand it anymore and finally asked me politely to stop chewing my nails. We were a pair of dueling nervous banjos.

I pulled into the parking lot slowly, adding to the overblown edginess of the mission. After cutting the engine I pointed out the entrance ahead and drew a diagram of the route to my bedroom on my thigh with my gnawed fingernail. Spill and Pinnopio: the most ragtag task force in the annals of special ops.

Bill hung on my words with electrocuted alertness, zapped by fear of this crazed Layne fellow and a subterranean thrill of adventure. His entire life, it was a sensation Ron had protected him from. Finally, before sucking in deep and storming the door, I instructed Bill to "be cool" and to "let me do the talking". The tactlessness of the latter directive was lost in the heat of the moment.

With Bill pulling up the rear and me, key ready, measuring my final approach to the door, I prayed Layne would be anyplace but upstairs. My prayer was answered when, in a single motion, the doorknob slipped from my slack grip and Layne's spindly hand acted as surrogate.

"Return of the nine-to-fiver," he said boisterously, not yet sobered from our morning *Cleanse*. I backed away into Bill, fleeing from the shake, and Layne stepped forward to garrison the space I'd created. Bill stepped aside. Our three shadows on the ground gave away nothing of the situation. "Ah, the work mobile. So, pal, who's your partner?" Layne asked effervescently.

"OK, so, this here is Bill. Bill, this here is Layne," I sputtered. Mere seconds after imploring Bill to be cool. Bill was swift in raising his open hand shoulder high, nipping the possibility of a contact greeting.

"How. Me Layne," Layne said lightheartedly, matching Bill's salute.

Scratching his arms and jangling in his work boots, Bill struggled to contain himself. I was to blame, for treating the small move like we were D-Day troops storming the beach at Normandy.

"The toi-toi-toi-johnny?" Bill asked smartly.

"Go on up Bill. It's right where I showed you," I said, scanning Layne in my periphery for a reaction. Lead by his memory of the map on my thigh Bill made for the bedroom. Layne looked at me inquisitively, wondering why I would brief Bill on the location of the facilities prior to our arrival, but guesswork apparently suggested to him an emergency.

I remained. We talked weather. I fielded groundballs about my day 'in the trenches'. Layne thanked me for having an open mind that morning, calling me "a model friend". And out walked Bill, parting us with a bag of golf clubs and a duvet slung from his arms.

Inquisitive pleats returned to Layne's face.

"The thing is…," I said.

The thing is is the fountainhead of all bad news, and I had no follow-through. Unrehearsed, no prefab speech arrived from which to pluck. Layne's eyes kept time to my fumbling like the hands of a fob watch.

Close. Close. Close. Don't take no for an answer. Under-promise and over-deliver. A good seller knows when to dispense the aspirin; little white lies, only when necessary. Bert's drill-bits rolled my eyes like slot-machine symbols. **Cherry-Seven-Lemon-Liberty Bell. Cherry-Seven-Lemon-Liberty Bell. Cherry-Seven-Lemon-Liberty Bell.** *Something has to catch!*

"I gotta go too." I gave my crotch an emblematic pinch and blew Layne off with a prank call of Nature, escaping through the open door to the stairs. Layne followed behind me to the crest of hardwood. If he'd been on his way out, he had changed his mind.

Dinner for two simmered on the stovetop; the pong of canned tomato soup choked my breathing space. The living room — Layne's showroom floor – remained perennially spick and span.

"Layne, I can't take this anymore. I'm moving out," I said, yanking the pin.

Say anything but! You are moving home to Ontario. You are moving in with your sick Uncle Jerry to care for him. You got back together with Nic. You joined the Hare Krishna. You won the lottery. No. Stand your ground, wimp! Days of conning and woe. Shot at you from this loose cannon. You represent the wronged. Why should you let his ego down gently? I found out why. The answer came promptly: the grenade was live. Layne went skittish, this way and that, dragging his forehead into his hairline with stiff fingers. "What? Aw c'mon! Just like that? Just like *that!*" Layne cried. Bill, red-faced and dead on his feet, returned in time to hear Layne's bellow. It breathed new panic-stricken life into him and he skedaddled to my bedroom. "Nate, please. You've had a heavy morning. The false alarm with Ol' Cory. My coming clean. All I'm saying is don't be so *fucking* rash."

"Layne, I tried to."

"You tried to what? Where do you get off treating people like this?" he spat.

I drew my hands out of my pockets. Ready, just in case we came to blows.

"Hang on with the loading Gramps. We're talking this out." Bill had come out with three dresser drawers. Calculating his route with a backbreaker of a load in his arms, Bill proceeded to the stairs on forward momentum. Layne rushed his path. "Did you hear what I said old man? Take five!" Layne's open right hand rose swiftly and smacked down on Bill's load like a flyswatter. Bill hadn't had a firm grip on anything in his life, except possibly life itself, when he clung to it as a newborn on an oven door. The drawers came crashing to the floor. Though he was long accustomed to articles slipping from his grasp, Bill grew terribly flummoxed. "How 'bout you stop it with the goddam distractions, you stuttering old mule? Or do you wanna piece of me?" Layne cried. Bill backed up, trying to keep his distance.

"Layne. Layne!" I shouted in vain. Then inspiration struck.

Tweeeeeeeeeeeeeeee-errrrrr-eeeeeeeeeeeeeeeep!

My high four-finger whistle—a necessity in Briscoll's uproarious factory—halted Layne's indignant pursuit of Bill and bought me enough time to sideline him with a dose of what he so urgently wanted to hear.

"Layne! Stop it. Layne! Please. Look at me. You are totally right. Layne, I am out of line and way out in front of myself. I see that now. I've jumped the gun here. What we need, what we need is to sit down and sort this out. Please Layne. What say we step out the back, take a breather, and discuss this like friends. C'mon amigo," I said, in character.   Layne's eyes opened a hair more and unglued from Bill. His shoulders relaxed and his breath lengthened. The "friend" bit had hooked him. His turn at naivety.

"Bill, please. You mind putting my stuff back and chilling out in my room? Grab your smokes Layne. I'll have one too," I added, laying it on thick.

Vigilant, I let Layne step outside first to avoid getting trapped at the far end of balcony and also to slyly pass Bill a pinwheel wave of my finger telling him to carry on as planned. Then I stepped outside and closed the door behind me. Layne doled out the smokes. He put a plastic lighter under his own, then my, cigarette. We smoked, tacitly collecting ourselves. I tried my best not to hack on the fumes as the sickly unbalance of a non-smoker head rush took over my brain. Inside Bill worked as rapidly and as quietly as his age and dexterity would allow.

"You always smoked Du Maurier bro?" I asked Layne.

Layne leap-frogged my stall tactic. "You can't be living your life this way, jumping ship at the first sight of danger." His concern came over as corny, but his manner showed a wholehearted sincerity. "You're a bigger person than that Nate. I know I wasn't square with you from the start. But you would have vetoed this place had you known," he continued. "AIDS is my condition, not yours. It requires nothing of you and I can't give it to you. Sex and drugs, my friend, are its only couriers. We've had our laughs, haven't we? I'm the same guy you met two weeks ago." Layne's pleading told me he thought he stood a coin-toss chance of turning me around. In the process, he was doing a tremendous job of whiling away the time for Bill.

"Now Layne. I can't blame you for lying about your circumstance. But it is one house fire after another around here. I can't live like this. All things equal and our only rift being you lying about your health, I willingly stay," I lied. "But as it stands..."

"I need this man. More than you could ever know. I'm cleaning up my act. Honestly Nate. I'll give you the ready weed in there to sell. Please, don't leave me," Layne choked, a welling of tears in his eyes.

"Sorry but I've made up my mind," I said. I flicked my cigarette to the grass a floor below—then wished it back to the ashtray I spotted on the ledge. "There is too much to go back on, Layne."

Layne looked away, hiding his ache as I left him to go inside. I could see now that Nate and His Bland Life must have been a breath of fresh air to this whacked-out man. Deep down, in the deepest down, I sympathized with anyone so far gone.

In my old bedroom—now denuded of everything but a heavy box of books and old pictures I had yet to unpack—I pushed my white rubber bracelet down to my hand and scratched the tacky pale band of suppressed skin. "What is expected of me?" I asked open space. The white walls of Layne's paintjob peered back at me. *Is he troubled from neglect, or was he neglected for being troubled?* My pondering was short-lived though, deferred to the urgency of retreat. While Crazy Layne was busy wallowing in self-pity, I needed to attend to zero hour.

The last box had a loose bottom from a poor taping job, so I riveted the dorsal flaps and strained to lift it to a cartable level. Passing the bathroom I forbore collecting my toiletries, reasoning a stop at a drugstore was worth the economy of present time. I was too preoccupied with leaving for any final consideration of the room that might serve as the ending credits of a movie, my movie. The main thing was that Layne was keeping scarce and sufficiently shattered not to make a fuss.

I readjusted my grip on the heavy box and felt a tight burn in my shoulders and forearms as I made for the stairs. The first step was dauntingly out of sight below the box. I gauged the drop with a scouting toe. I would be piloted by muscle memory and feel from there on in. Two more steps of faith and Layne emerged at my side, sprung from his foxhole.

I could pace only as fast as feeling with my feet would permit me. He moored himself to my side and lit into me in a guttural snarl. "You fucking backstabber," he sneered. Startled, I slipped a step and nearly tumbled the remainder, rallying my balance for a glance at his face. Layne's eyes had gone bloodshot from rubbing, and contours of vein and muscle protruded from his tensed neck. It was a face mangled by illness, hard drugs, and fury: he embodied that scarred spinning head of the building itself. Spittle gleamed at the sides of his mouth and BB's of it pelted the left side of my neck and face. I felt each pellet sting as if it was a red-hot cinder.

Drop the box! I demanded of myself. We were crammed

too close on the narrow stairs for me to see his hands. Visions of heroin-prepped needles spiking my carotid artery kept me searching. *Drop the box!* "Let this go Layne. Please," I said. I used the consoling tone offered to jumpers on ledges.

"No, you let it go." Layne would not be talked down. He unified his steps with mine. "This how you treat a buddy? Huh, amigo? I oughta right you. Right here and now. You disloyal piss ant." A barrage of saliva.

Drop the box!

But for the life of me, I could not unshackle my hands. At the time I thought my only course was direct to the doorknob. No sudden movements. Drop the box and I might startle Layne into an act that, until then, may only have been contemplation. Dropping the box signified that escalating violence was not only possible in my world, but the time for it had come. Dropping the box meant accepting danger and facing it head on.

Dropping the box was out of my range. Drop the box and the bottom falls out!

A firm lifelong lament, me not dropping that box. Not letting fly some books and a photo archive of dated haircuts to protect myself in a clutch. As I lined myself up with the doorknob at last, Layne stopped on the bottom step and disappeared behind me.

Realizing I was at my most vulnerable, I crooked my right leg like a flamingo and rested the box between it and the wall. I jerked the knob and sunlight fell onto the landing. Propping the door with my foot, I halted abruptly, aware of a piercing assault on my left shoulder blade.

"Nothing more than a dirty fucking traitor." Layne's voice had lowered, calmed by physical release. Again I was stabbed, this strike nearer my middle back. "You lost? Get off my property," he said.

My knee joints unhitched with the sensation that they might bend in any given direction. The box, my crutch to the finish, stayed in my arms. Each stab wound pulsed as I turned to face my attacker. A third blow fell on my upper right arm. His weapon now came into view.

"You deaf? Get out. Fuck off and die!" Layne slammed the

door inches from my box, leaving me outside. I felt faint and sick to my stomach. Layne's weapon of choice? The harm he'd stealthily brandished down those stairs?

The overgrown fingernail on his right index finger.

WE UNLOADED THE VAN'S CONTENTS ONTO A SKID
attached to lift truck #2. I welcomed Ron's karmic drenching as
he chided me for blowing the roof off Bill's safe haven. Ron had
overheard Kevin talking about Layne to the guys in the plant.
Giant in his steel-toed boots, daring himself to punch my head
clean from my body, he described how he would watch it roll off
the loading dock, through the empty parking lot, along the steep
gradient of the street, and bob down the Fraser River. He snarled:
"Next time, get your own hands dirty and dig *yourself* out!" Ron's
contempt was lost in the fog of my discouragement, as if he were
unclear and coming at me from a faraway place, just radio static.

The same cannot be said for Nic going out on a date with a
coworker the very same evening—some jerk I met at one of her
work functions. I knew this because I was forced to plead for a
night's stay on her couch.

She returned home late, in a slim-fit cocktail dress and dark
seductive eye makeup, in perfume that smelt like strawberry
marshmallow candies, and called me off the couch into bed with
her.

Standing in the middle of the bedroom she shed all of her
clothes as though I wasn't even there. Her nude silhouette played
with the murky dark. *A pity lay?* I thought. How demeaning. And

rare. *She's sloshed. I'm not. This isn't right.*

I joined her anyway. Nic crashed onto her side of the bed and passed out like I wasn't ever there.

THE NEXT DAY I WAFFLED IN MY OFFICE UNTIL RON

left on a supply run. Then I stole around the plant checking to see if my stash had been dispatched into a drum of industrial-strength acid, or the dumpster out back, or postmarked with a shipment slated for China. Lucky for me there it lay: a shrink-wrapped plank of curbside furniture and tired clothing and oh damn but oh well, Layne's cruddy tabletop stereo. And no doubt somewhere in there, his tasselly leather jacket. All of it tucked way back in aisle 6C with the bastardized mis-tints.

That very hour, Chantelle transferred a cheerful caller to my office phone line.

"This is Nate. How can I help you?"

"You can help me by returning the set I lent you," the familiar voice said back.

"Layne?"

"Right-e-o smart guy. Thought you got away with it, didn't you?"

I thought back to the day I'd taped my business card to the lid of his paint sample. "Look, I didn't know Bill packed your radio and jacket until an hour ago."

"Too late for that now. Steps have been taken."

"Steps? What steps?"

"Steps. Already called VPD and filed a claim. Consider your ass nailed to the wall," he said matter of factly.

Fed up with Layne's antics and braver on the phone, I aped a scared little boy: "Oh please Layne, call off the dogs. A pipsqueak like me would get eaten alive in the clink." Layne breathed heavy breaths in the receiver as I carried on. "What's the charge? Theft under five dollars?" I mocked. "By the way, I want Mr. Chin's number to get my damage deposit back, and the clothes I left in the laundry room."

Layne laughed me off. "You signed a binding contract recognized by the Vancouver Tenancy Act. Thirty days' notice to get back that money. You gave thirty seconds. Kiss that money bye-bye."

Well played, I thought. "What, that yellow doodle-pad?" Talks were breaking down.

"Says right here 900 Murray Street," Layne read, starting to scream madly. "I'M COMING DOWN THERE TO RIP YOUR FUCKING FACE OFF! YOU'RE FUCKING DEAD!" *Click.*

Gossip had begun to circulate around the office about my misadventure, so I kept Layne's threat a secret. I left the office that day with the five o'clock horde, dogging it to Nic's as fast as my legs could pedal, sporadically checking my tail.

For the following five workdays life at Nic's became more burdensome and Layne became harder to ignore, averaging 1.8 death threats per day.

"You'll be dead by the end of the day!"

"I'll make a new leather jacket out of your skin!"

"I've decided to soak you with gasoline and set you on fire, so you can burn on earth before you burn in hell!"

His last was impossible to pass over. It had embroiled my manager and my ex. On April 11, 2001 at 9:37 a.m., a man kindly asked reception for the voicemail of Nathan Mills's supervisor. Chantelle obliged him without appeal, and in a stately tone, he left Bert this message: *"Good day Mr. Francis. You don't know who I am but my name is Layne Rhodes. I was the roommate of your employee,*

Nathan Mills, until he decided to break his lease. I am obliged to inform you that Mr. Mills has absconded with several of my most valued possessions including a leather jacket, a sound system and a gold watch, a Rhodes family heirloom. News of this sort, about a trusted colleague, should come as a shock to you. Trust that it surprised me also, after falling for Nate's small town charm.

"I didn't want it to come to this, but I've enlisted the police. The only contact information I had for Nate was his place of business, so they may decide to intercept him there. My apologies for any distraction this may cause. Thank you for your time. Good day." Click.

And on April 11, 2001 at 9:39 a.m., the man left this message in my voice mailbox: "Time to look for a new job, 'cause guess who I just called? Your boss, Bert Francis. It's time people started seeing past your horseshit. Say, how's your ex-lady Nic. Think it's time I make a house call to Miss Potty Mouth. You know— have my fun before this ends. She told me where she worked that day she was here by the way. What's the matter Nate? Your life in ruin? How does it feel? Fuck if you think I'm done. You'll know it's over when I'm standing over your dying body. You little fuck-face!" Click.

Two middle-aged policemen arrived at Briscoll Inc. later that same day, at *my* solicitation. Heads poked out of office doors like a choreographed Broadway musical as they strutted down the hallway to my office where Bert and I were sitting. The two acted official as I played the two saved messages on speakerphone and edified them with my Layne Story (only the pertinent clippings). The stockier one asked the questions, the other scribbled notes.

"How did you find this Layne Rhodes?"

"The Classifieds." I spoke with my neck in my hand, sounding ridiculous.

"A cop from that beat was already dispatched to Grandview Highway North. Turns out they know the guy. Plenty of disturbances, no convictions. A harmless quack. You did the right thing by calling us. Play it safe for the next few days, do not engage him, and you and your girlfriend will be fine."

"She's not my girlfriend."

"Pardon?"

"She's not my girlfriend, not anymore."

"Oh, sorry about that bud." The recording cop scrawled this note in his notepad.

Their last order of business was to repo the stereo and jacket. Ron was none too impressed having to fork the load down and watch me tear into the shrink-wrap. Led by Kevin's inventive cracks, the fellas in the plant enjoyed a hearty laugh at my expense. Even the note-taking officer let out an undisciplined choke when he saw the flamboyant jacket emerge.

"And *my* clothes?" I asked.

"I'd write them off if I were you. The kook probably soiled them, or worse," the talker said. I wanted to challenge him on what he meant by 'or worse', because certainly a burning or shredding would be better, not worse.

They also informed me that recovering my rent and damage deposit was out of their jurisdiction and to bring the matter to the Vancouver Tenancy Board.

And meet Layne at a hearing? Tempt him to rip my face off?

I wrote off my rent and deposit right then and there. Added to my clothes and the good will groceries, I was out fifteen hundred dollars in five days—the cost of a roundtrip airline ticket to Australia.

By day's end, Briscoll Inc. was abuzz with both the factual bits and filler bobs to what had now officially become my Layne Story.

"You hear? Nate is dealing drugs."

"You hear? Nate is a witness in a murder investigation."

"You hear? Nate is being stalked by his ex-lover. A man!"

"You hear? Nate is HIV-positive."

THE HEAT WAVE ENDED AND WITH IT WENT LAYNE'S

infatuation with my slow death. Overcast skies and rain reestablished their dominance over season and conversation. Dennis returned from Europe plump with stories—none however juicier than my Layne Story. Right away he offered his couch to save me from Nic.

The infallible press of time brought on a dry summer—a second summer, as it were. Ideal weather for exterior painting; prime time for movers of commercial paints. I spent the warm season chasing orders that refused to be outrun, scrutinizing ATM receipts, moving into Uncle Jerry's basement, not missing Celine Dion's radical passion (she was on a self-imposed career break at the time), batching homebrew and attending parties hosted by Dennis Zimmer and graced by a motley trove of esteemed guests.

There was Luke, the head-and-neck surgeon with a weekend addiction to ecstasy and nitrous oxide. T.C., the set designer and Scrabble cultist. Melissa, the CFO for a Western Canadian chain of dessert cafes. Riff, the tattoo artist who lived for documentaries. Cairn, the Vancouver Island sculptress and mother of two adopted children. And Parks. And Shannon. And Demone. And so on. In they came and out they went, leaving at party's end, each with their own mental illustrations to my Layne Story.

Seasons, like kleptomaniacs, rarely depart empty-handed. The summer ended my sentence at Briscoll Inc. I handed Bert my official two week notice on September 12th, 2001, one day after the delirium of Nine-Eleven. Standing over a bowl of pulpy corn flakes, I watched in horror the live telecast of the second plane entering the north tower. I struggled to digest what I was witnessing, for the first time on equal footing with Uncle Jerry who stood next to me with slack jaw in his designer three-piece and gold watch. I typed my notice that same afternoon, astounded and chagrinned by the ease of it.

My intention was met with modest resistance: it was a miracle to most that I hadn't already been axed. As the culmination of a long-standing joke between friends, I dropped a note on Dennis's desk that read: **My days are so effing over, dude!**

I HARBOURED THE NOTION THAT A STURDIER FRAME-work of jet plane was surely required for air travel over international waters. It would be needed to traverse the demonic hurricane and cyclone patterns of the Pacific. So I was numbed, when boarding at LAX, to see merely a larger version of the Fischer Price plane I'd ridden from Toronto to Los Angeles.

In a set of travel guides bought for ten bucks at a used bookstore I checked off landmarks I'd long desired to visit. Jotting down goals for my new life kept my mind off present-day aeronautics. Translated to paper my checklist was daunting.

1. **Find yourself.**
2. **Discover your hidden talent and a career that coincides.**
3. **Find a lifelong companion.**
4. **Forgive yourself for laying it on thick about Layne to your family and friends. Consider coming clean.**
5. **Find a hobby that gets you in shape and that people think cool (Surfing? Hang gliding?). Get really good at it.**
6. **Shake the depression and be happy every single day.**

One year later, I have managed to relax in the shadow cast by my mandate's unmet expectations. Encounters with strangers, and group e-mails to home, help. In fact my reveries from faraway lands have led family and friends to think of me as an adventurer—an identity I admit to relishing, though thousands embark on it every day and one could hardly call it daring.

According to my fifteen compounded e-diaries, in less than eleven months I have torn through Australian, New Zealand, and South East Asian landscapes with the intensity of an eco-challenge racer and the drivenness of a religious missionary, getting myself into all flavours of situations. Cliff diving at The Grotto with the Gaelic football squad from Dublin and their tag-along happy-to-be-anywhere cheerleaders; and crushing cases of Victoria Bitter beer while laughing in the hot sun formed my showpiece, the most superb of my e-mails home. Read and re-read to myself in the internet café, I buffed it until it shone.

Life on the road has had its swells and shallows. What was it that Layne read to me when we first met? Oh yes, *Save the brute agony of humanity, we wring out a dewdrop of existence and salve our burns with periodic forgetfulness.*

Yep, he actually did that.

Part Five

Quick Tips for a Flawless Do-It-Yourself Painting Experience

Step 5:

Step back and enjoy what you've created. If you notice any imperfections, do not dwell on them. Many can occur naturally and are simply unavoidable. You can always fix them with a recoat somewhere down the road. Be proud of yourself and your accomplishment.

I KNOW THERE IS UNFINISHED BUSINESS. QUESTIONS

pressing. Why lie? Why fatten an otherwise bloated creampuff of an anecdote?

Layne ran up one side of me and down the other. The dick drove a combine through my twenty-fourth year. Relieved me of fifteen hundred dollars—my Australian nest-egg—and sent me groveling, hat in hand, back to Nic of all people. And for a seven-day encore threatened to sex Nic and relieve me of my face.

As is, my Layne Story is a stand out. A party-grabber. End of story. So again it begs: why lie? Why deceive your friends, family, even your own mother, for no good reason? It makes no sense to elaborate such a harrowing tale any further. It's pointless, sort of like stoning the dead.

C'mon Nate, off like a band-aid.

The truth and literally.

Here goes nothing.

Layne is a figment of my imagination and is now a figment of yours.
Shit.

It happened again. I'm sorry.

Layne Rhodes is actually a young man named Cory Lane. That is to say, Cory Lane is Layne Rhodes. I made Layne Rhodes up, basing him loosely on my old Vancouver roommate: close friend and confidante Cory Lane.

It may seem offhand of me to carry on storytelling after wasting the time, faith and sympathy of so many, but here we are. Trust that I started out this confession with the purest of intentions and please allow me to set the record straight once and for all. Please. I had my reasons for lying.

Cory was a vintage soul. No moustache though. "A cryogenically frozen twenty-four-year-old from the Forties," I'd rag him in fun. After Cory showered at night, on went his PJ's, robe and slippers. Wet hair parted left. And every morning he ate a bowl of fibre cereal and whole wheat toast smeared with a thick lamina of marmalade he bought in bulk. "Unclogs the pipes," he'd boast.

In the week prior to my viewing the apartment, Cory introduced himself over the telephone as a member and sponsored grower of Vancouver's Compassion Club, and survivor of a one year-old diagnosis of Hodgkin's Disease—one of the most curable types of cancer (Seventy-five percent cure rate for all, ninety percent cure rate for younger patients. I googled it right after we had hung up. Hodgkin's had afflicted Canadian hockey legend Mario Lemieux. Lemieux underwent chemotherapy and was back on the ice two months later). Cory was in remission and reported a clean bill.

"Grandview Highway North is a block south of Broadway and Commercial, right?" I asked. Cory had picked up on my trepidation through the receiver.

"You got 'er. This is the East Side we're talking brotha, so be sure to wear neutral colours, whites and beiges only! — Listen to me, talking to you like I'm your grandmother or something. I'm sorry, Nate is it?" he said candidly. *Who is this guy?* I thought, already regretting my decision to view the place.

But from minute one Cory's sense of humour won me over. "I'll show you the bathroom first. You circumcised?" he asked, letting me fidget in discomfort before displaying the shower's turbo-pressure. "'Cause you will be. You dabble in the sex trade? Of course you do. Who doesn't, right? You'll find the 'tutes around here pricey. But what you pay there you make back in cheap rent here." Cory said while showing me the spare bedroom, a hooded expression on his face. "But don't get me wrong, clock-watchers the girls are not. They provide a wire-to-wire carpet ride and they always get you to your destination, if you catch my drift." Cory winked slyly, doing a great Bert Francis though they had never met.

Cory also showed me the "Howse Rools" — a hand-written list of regulations from his Japanese landlord, Mr. Ohama. Mr. Ohama was a pleasant first generation Canadian with a get-by grasp of the English language. Howse Rool number seven was Cory's favourite: *No lowd noyses pass ten-turty (i.e. blendy drink, kettel whissels).*

"There's the deal-breaker: no green tea smoothies after ten-turty. They always walk after hearing number seven," he said, deadpan.

The apartment construction and its thrift store decor was the same as I've described in my Layne Story, macramé owl included. Cory was a bit of a flea market addict. On the hallway wall that linked the two bedrooms hung a gothic black and white portrait in an antique frame of Cory's great-great-grandfather, Archibald Lane, as a toddler. The expressionless boy had a flattop boater hat on his head — still a part of standard garb in some Australian private schools — and, befitting the era, a dress over his little body. He held an English handbell in one hand and a shepherd's staff in the other. Though I never said so, I found the portrait unsettling. No — upsetting. The thing haunted me. Twice I swore I saw the boy's eyes move, and every time I speed-walked past, I imagined the shepherd's staff collaring my neck and dragging me into the painting for all of eternity. Prizing the Lane family heirloom,

Cory referred to it as "a lesson in humility". He gave me another lesson that first weekend when he took me to "Sunday Supper" at the shelter.

Sunday Supper was a community centre gymnasium, set up with tables to serve a warm meal to the less fortunate. Beneath its north end basketball hoop from behind a fold-out banquet table, Cory, in one of his centrally-themed T-shirts, helped me spoon chow from cast iron kettles onto paper plates and receive the weak, grateful smiles of hungry mouths. To add a touch of civility to their heart-straining poverty, grace was said by a slender man with a brown mullet and a matching push-broom moustache. Rain rattled the gymnasium rooftop, and he raised his arms up as if looking to embrace the entire congregation. Given his purple button-up and beige slacks, he failed to score in the fashion department, but he did exemplary work with his homily: "Please feel free to keep on eating as I speak. The indifference of circumstance has put you people in unwieldy predicaments. Let's pray for a shift in the balance that favours us all. Thank you for opening yourselves to our charity. Although we cannot sympathize with your situations, we do empathize. In the name of the Father, Son and Holy Ghost. Amen."

Blank name cards had been propped in front of disposable utensils and paper napkins. On loan from Christmas, paper tablecloths with red poinsettias had been taped to the long community tables and every four seats sat a tin water jug, a stack of four disposable cups and four crayons.

Many revered Cory—including another fixture at Sunday Supper, a short mentally ill man whom Cory had nicknamed Manners (to Manners's sheer delight). Manners was obese from meds. His body type, however, did not stall him dashing, clammy, around the room, gruffly imploring proper table decorum. "Germs linger on the fingers!" and "Fork left, knife right!" he'd repeat insistently. From time to time if Manners felt etiquette was seriously lagging in the room, he became agitated and would scream. In his frazzled state the stipulations became condensed to "Linger finger!' or 'Forleft, knifight!' Cory thrice had to settle Manners by calling him over and putting to him a routine set of questions: "Hey Manners, bud," said Cory, his thin arm on Manners's back.

"Yah Cory?" Manners replied with child-like innocence. I watched the scene in awe, my big metal spoon submerged in a *Green Giant* corn-carrot-pea medley.

"Do you know where an oyster fork goes?"

Manners twisted his hair in his fingers and looked down at his shoes smiling. "Up your ass, Cory," Manners said, trying desperately to bottle his snickers.

"Ah, so that's where it goes," Cory said in put-on seriousness, adding to Manners's delight. "And Manners, what about a soup spoon?"

Manners gazed downward again. "Up your ass, Cory!"

"I might be running out of room up there bud. Think you could do your pal Cory a big favour and be quieter on your rounds? Could you do that for me, huh Manners?"

"Yah Cory."

"Thanks my man," Cory said, offering a high hand. The stoutly Manners would give Cory a high-five and a free hug around his waist with eyes tenderly shut before setting out into the unmannerly fray.

To close the meal the same man who had opened it with prayer spoke to the room once again. "I hope you all enjoyed Aunt Caz's Irish stew. I know I sure did. You see the tables along the wall behind me with the cellophane and tinfoil wrapped plates. There are cookies and squares under them thanks to the volunteers at the Greater Vancouver Food Bank Society, and if I see any of you even looking in the direction of the door before approaching the dessert table," he said smiling, "I will have no choice but to pin you down and force feed you macaroons!

"Be safe. Make good choices. And may God be with all of you."

The daughter of a volunteer—a precious little thing named Tonya with black hair and green sparkles for eyes—smiled undaunted at the end of the dessert table, gifting from a straw basket the white rubber bracelets her mom helped her make. Each band had been enspirited with a single-word message in glittery block letters and childish depictions of rainbows, trees and happy stick-people. She blushed cutely when handing me mine with its three-letter word and its drawing of a bicycle. It made me miss my little brother from days gone by.

After the dishes were cleaned, and the tables broken down and trolleyed into the equipment room, Cory addressed my oblivious smiling. "Feels good, don't it?"

I sidetracked him with a story from St. Thomas about how Bako used to save up and let rip a fart at the foul line right before an opposing player had to shoot their free throws. We chuckled.

"Hard to tell who was helping who tonight," I said after.

"I come as often as I can."

"Where do the rest of these chairs go?" I asked, wanting to dam the gushiness.

"Up your ass, Nate."

Later that same evening we rented *The Big Lebowski*, watching it up close on Cory's twenty-inch television while tearing into the junk food we'd bought at the Safeway. Afterward Cory showed me an advertisement he had cut out for a forty-inch Sony Vega. "She'll be mine someday," he said. Broad eyes set on the future.

Off the top of my head I mentioned the prospect of him making the money by selling some of his weed crop. "There are a good handful of tokers in the office and nearly the entire Briscoll plant are chronics. Dennis alone could clear you out," I offered.

Cory acknowledged my generosity and went on to explain the noteworthy improvements the Compassion Club had made in the lives of its members, both in pain relief through the provision of clean, affordable cannabis—and in psychological sustenance —through support groups and caseworker sponsorship. His last give on the subject of backdoor selling was that he admired the strides the nonprofit British Columbia Compassion Club Society had made with the provincial and federal governments, and would not want to jeopardize the trust that they, and his fellow members, put in him both as a member and as a contracted grower. He said this without being preachy and not without accepting my idea as having been shared with the best of intentions, ensuring I'd feel like less of a jerk. "It's not like I haven't been tempted, but it's something you have to live through to understand. No offense taken whatsoever."

That was Cory. An amenable cohort and a warm friend. We were instantaneous mates, of which there is a dearth in a lifetime.

Helping us along was my lack of friendships in Vancouver— zero. Nic fell away and Dennis was becoming inaccessible: Briscoll Inc. was dispatching him to faraway lands more frequently, and there was this player from his Ultimate Frisbee team with whom he'd gone private. Cory had no wider a social circle than I did. He was outstandingly close with his sister Jo (Josephine) and no-one else. Yet our shared fire would have caught without the lack of other light.

And it was on display the following morning when those three boys happened upon the dead man in the tree across the street.

It had rained heavily that April. On this particular day, the clouds were daring us to tread under its heaving blanket of grey. Cory and I had planned an early start at his favourite eatery on The Drive: an oxymoronic vegan diner. "Popular with the truckers," Cory joked.

We ate and carried on to Compassion Club headquarters, also on Commercial Drive, just south of Broadway. While Cory continued inside, I was asked to sit in a waiting room.

It was a warm receiving area with Pumpkin Patch (777-99) walls and Ocean Pearl (123-88) drapes, a forestry of potted foliage and stacks of holistic literature. The amiable receptionist, Keja, a flowy, pretty girl with reptilian eyes and thick dreadlocks tamed under a pink bandana, explained to me why I was held back. "We are a respected, members-only club operating in a grey area of the law. To protect the sanctity and legitimacy of our cause, we do not allow general access to the offices, distribution centre, consumption lounge, dispensary, or wellness centre." She went on to detail the natural health care available to members at a sliding rate. Services were offered by licensed acupuncturists, reiki and yoga instructors, nutritionists, shiatsu therapists, energy healers, and Traditional Chinese Medicine practitioners.

Cory led his BCCCS compatriots out to the waiting room to meet his new roommate. They further elucidated the work of the staff and I was moved by their sense of purpose, charity and, for lack of a better word, compassion.

On the walk home, though the skies were still a glum tarp of swelled cloud, I had a soft bounce to my step as if the sidewalks were laid with mattresses. I was still buzzing from the headiness of Sunday Supper and the activism of the Compassion Club. This is what I had had in mind when I was trying to bust out of Kitsilano. Why I had decried the pulse of the area. I wanted to live my life with eyes wide open.

Over the railway bridge, under the SkyTrain tracks, around the corner and down the security fence on Grandview Highway North, Cory and I said not a word and were not in the least discomfited by doing so. The mountains in the distance were obscured by cloud and I lightly measured the absurdity of that vast imposing range simply being tucked away until three rambunctious boys on BMX bikes, hurtling rocks over the security fence across from our building, rattled our tranquility.

Cory briefed me on approach. "These little weed mongers loiter outside the Club, trying to buy from terminally ill members. No shame!" he exclaimed. "Yo, whassup boyeez," Cory called out to them. They were a bicycle gang of three white kids no older than twelve who wore pants eight times the size of their hairless matchstick legs and ball caps with the brims tilted upward at forty-five degrees. One brim was studded with rhinestones that spelled **Fitty O.G.** Tellingly, their eyes were bloodshot.

"Nuffin' dawg," the first child said with attitude.

"Nuffin'? Playa found him a capped daddy," the second child, the apparent leader, said, with his eyes fixed to the fence. Floored and amused by their vocabularies and bogus inner city accents, I stood speechless with intrigue.

"S'up homies?" Cory continued.

"You know, G-money. Blop! Blop! Blop!" The third child

interpreted, miming a pistol with a thumb and two fingers.

"Seriously guys, if I don't get some damn English soon, me and my friend Nate here are going to slash your tires, OK?" Cory was through wit' playin'.

"Guy's dead," the third one said, toning it down, pointing his little index finger to the fence. Beyond about fifty feet, a man sprawled in a vintage grey suit, his extremities hidden in the long grass and his head out of sight behind a tree.

Cory was over the barricade in a jiffy, something the three with the bald genitalia were no doubt daring themselves to do but were too scared. The boys held quiet, visibly agitated by Cory's proximity to the body. As was I, Sally Struthers.

"He's a goner alright. You wouldn't believe the smell. *Whew-wee!* Like white vinegar and moldy cheese! And the bugs! All in his nose and mouth," Cory exclaimed. I could tell by his drama there was no body in that suit. Subtleties of tone like toots on a dog whistle that the youngsters did not hear or had yet to learn.

"His neck looks cut, like they tried to decapitate him or something!"

The boys were wood-stiff. They had taken the bait, like the fish humans in Bako's screenplay. It required every gram of concentration from me not to blow Cory's game by bursting into laughter.

"Wa-wa-was he stabbed?" the leader asked. Hooliganism had been scared right out of him, the demon at an exorcism.

"Was he ever! With the looks of things, my guess is we'll find others in this field," Cory said.

The kids' Adam's apples shot up with every dry gulp.

"What say we have some fun with this one? Jump on his belly and see if anything oozes out of him?"

"Do it," I egged. "Bet you his eyes pop out."

"Oh I'm doing it." Cory took three steps back and readied himself like a runner at a starting line. On the verge of seeing a decaying dead man used for a trampoline, the tikes had become petrified, blown away by how crazy big folk could be. Cory charged the body with two flagrant strides and bending at the knees for a heartier frog-stomp, took air.

"No!" one cried in a piglet squeal. The other two cringed in their parachute clothing.

Cory came down with a hard thump and feigned bodily fluids squirting back up into his eye. He allowed time for the boys to squirm before kicking the stack of clothing out from the grass.

"Whoops! My mistake. Just a bunch of old abandoned suits!" He stuck his last line. A virtuoso performance.

"Bravo!" I called through convulsive laughter.

"There's a lesson in all this lads: don't smoke drugs. They make you think you are black and make you see dead people. So stop mooching swizzle sticks outside the Club! *And*, what else?"

The boys stared blankly.

"Never dive headfirst into unknown waters. Now you three move along so that my associate and I can get these garments appraised. Go on, git!" The boys peddled off, sufficiently chastened.

Abdominal muscles aching, I swiped salty tears from my face as Cory shimmied up and back down the fence.

"Never dive headfirst into unknown waters?" I said.

"What? It's important. Ever see those *PLAYSAFE* videos? Scare the shit out of you."

"You're messed. And that shirt," I said breaking down into another fit of laughter. Cory had amassed a collection of over thirty marijuana themed T-shirts. The one he wore that day, Hockey Undershirt (940-00), featured the venerated cartoon character Popeye the Sailor Man. On the front it showed a cherry-eyed Popeye, packing his corncob pipe with his spuriously huge forearms. He held, not a can of spinach, but weed in a plastic baggy. The caption underneath read: **I'm strong to the finish, 'cause I smokes me spinach. I'm Popeye the Toker Man. Toot! Toot!** On the back, another caption read: **I yam what I yam, and that's all that I yam.**

We got on like soul brothers for the next five days. In that span Cory introduced me to downstairs tenants Mr. & Mrs. Holme and Mark. Mrs. Holme—Marnie rather (she insisted I call her

Marnie)—a legitimate school teacher with a wily bank of curly black hair, lived directly below us. She was a darling woman and a gifted conversationalist. She owned two Shih Tzu puppies, Stanley and Cindy, and spoke candidly of her infertility as "the brakes". Marnie kept a lawn chair, a golf umbrella, a pair of wide-lens sunglasses, and a doggy bed. Rain or shine, Marnie, Stanley and Cindy would open themselves to the elements to brave mommy's habit: Mr. Holme, a pastry chef for the Vancouver Hotel (his aromatics regularly wafted up into our apartment) demanded she go outside if she insisted on smoking her toxic cigarillos. I revered our transitory chats, getting the urge to call my Mom straight after one of our heart to hearts.

Mark lived where Pretend Mark lived. He drove truck and was seldom seen around the building—sleeping during the day, his internal clock set to traffic's low tide. For this Cory nicknamed him 'Polkaroo', after the slippery character in the children's TV series *Polka Dot Door*. The day I met Mark Cory had clipped an advertisement for curtains out of a Canadian Tire flyer and presented it to him. "Please. Summer is fast approaching and we don't want you scaring the children again," Cory said. Mark laughed maniacally and said that he'd get right on it. Cory later divulged that the previous summer, Mark, sleeping days and roasting in the heat, sought relief by stripping down to his briefs and opening his sliding glass door, drawing the curtain for privacy. The problem lay in the voile mosquito net material from which his curtains were cut. They'd floated upward on the lamest of breezes, giving fellow tenants the optical shock of a hairy, three-hundred pound, sleep-apneal trucker in his XXXL tighty whities.

Cory and I got on so well he launched into notions that I date his kid sister. Take it from a guy with two sisters, it is a ponderous and flattering suggestion. "Forget firemen, she's always going on about paint salesmen," he teased.

From a young age, contrary to the natural order of sibling rivalry, Cory and Jo were devout friends. She lived close by and from what I was led to believe but had yet to see, visited with greater frequency than the mail carrier.

"Even more often when her ex-boyfriend Duffy lived here," Cory mentioned. He was wearing his **Thank you for pot smoking** T-shirt, the one crowned as the groundbreaker in his T-shirt anthology. "Duffy had issues with me and she dropped him like that." He snapped his fingers. "Jo said we were a package deal. She can be a real hard-ass when she wants to be."

Cory was tightlipped about the issues Duffy'd had with him, so I didn't push. I assumed maybe Cory's cancer had scared him away and thought nothing more about him. Until I saw a photograph of the fair Josephine. Then I thought Duffy to be the stupidest man alive.

"On second thought, don't even bother. Pretty girl like Jo has no time to humour paint geeks," Cory added in fun.

We would eventually meet in passing, Jo and I, but only in passing.

Cory admitted to choosing Hodgkin's because of its reputation as a pushover disease. Feeling ashamed for tricking me and secure enough in our companionship, he led me to the covered back porch one rainy morning seven days into my tenure to tell me his real situation: diagnosed with HIV in 1996 at the unripe age of twenty due to unprotected sex with a multi-partnered carrier. The medicinal marijuana from the Club kept his nausea down and his appetite steady.

He apologized for lying. Said he didn't want the HIV to cloud my judgment of him. Spoke of moving forward and worked to calm any fear by giving me two pamphlets from the Compassion Club. His case worker's idea.

"Warning, the following literature will put a damper on any Heroin Scrabble nights you were planning. Also, somewhere near the back, it says we can't bone. That means no matter how much you turn my crank with that sexy paint knowledge, no boning. That goes double for BJ's," he said, trying to lighten the leaden air.

Melting inside, I forced an unconvincing smile, glossy leaflets creasing in my taut white fingers. Cory stayed his rehearsed course, giving me the dirt on his wealthy ultra-right-wing parents and their struggle to deal with his illness socially. Dave and Terry Lane, in their own eyes, had lost a son to homosexuality, drug abuse or whoredom—take your pick. They were left with one clean progeny, period. The Lanes, along with most of Cory's highbrow childhood friends stayed true to their colours and distanced themselves from his sentence, fading to the periphery of his life and eventually disappearing past the foggy margin. His sister Jo, a standing rock amidst the blowing sand, held her ground beside her elder brother, eventually forfeiting her financial birthright by disowning their parents.

Recalling the calamity of that year pressed two tears from Cory's eyes, dampening a week of bonding over humanitarianism and skin-deep folly. The deviation of Cory's mood, set to a background plop of guttered rain poking holes in the wet earth, was gut-wrenching.

With a stiff slurp Cory sucked back his emotion and continued. "I'm not a charity case. I don't need a sponsor. I *am* sorry I lied and I *am* sorry I thought I had to. Flat out: you're a good one. We get on. I hope you can stay," he finished.

I took his offered hand, but gave no clues to an answer.

At the end of that work day I logged out the blimpy Briscoll van, drove it through untiring sprits of rain to Grandview Highway North, and broke my news to Cory, avoiding his intent blue eyes in favour of his cowlick part. "I wish you had been straight from the start. Things may have played out different. Living in such close quarters, honesty is everything."

Audacities. Weedy excuses as they were, instead of pecking them apart Cory let my b.s. stand. "I understand," he simply said. "I'm sorry it has to be this way Nate."

Hearing my name drew me from the semi-conscious disassociation people summon to get bad deeds done, into complete ownership, where I felt lower than the deepest down.

He'd strongly wanted for this friendship to work. I saw it in his eyes. A comrade his own age, an unforced connection outside the lines of counsellor, neighbour, or sibling. A stick to jam into the revolving door. He'd thought me different from Duffy, his parents and the rest. So had I. Downcast, he removed himself to the back porch as I withdrew in seven listless trips to the van.

When he returned indoors Cory was resolute in lending a hand with my heavy dresser—a two-man weight I'd contemplated leaving behind. We rallied to each end of it and heaved together on three. Handcuffed to the chest of drawers, my eyes faced his over its crest. I took the vulnerable lead down the stairs. I felt a screaming urge to let go. Even more, I wanted Cory to do me the service. *Let go Cory!* I willed him to drop his share and let the wood box come down on me, crushing my weak backbone. I wanted him to call me a coward out of a frothing mouth. Look at me with bloodshot eyes and ask me who I thought I was. Tell me I was a disloyal piss ant and a dirty traitor. Poke me in the back and tell me to F-off and die. He said no such things and helped lower my dresser down. He put a hand on my shoulder from behind me as I walked to the driver-side door. A dagger would have felt less painful.

"If you are ever jonesing for that game of Scrabble, you know where I'm at," he said through my rolled-down window. I nodded as he stepped back to the walkway, out of the rain.

A woman driving a rusty Pontiac 6000 bounded into the parking lot, scraping her undercarriage until her back tires made the grade. She skidded to a stop next to the Briscoll van and jumped out. I recognized her from the photo, even with the frantic red face and puffy eyes from crying.

"You Nate?" she barked. I dipped my eyes to the dashboard, ashamed to lay claim to my own name.

"Leave it Jo. Let him go," Cory said calmly. *He must have called her on the cordless, needing to talk*, I thought aimlessly.

"I rushed over here," she continued, breathless, "to ask you one question." Jo tried to keep her composure, shaking like a quill pen scratching on paper. But she succumbed, sobbing painful tears; making a dismal image in my window frame. Finally, wiping mucus from her nose, she offered her question: "Where do y-you get off hur-hur-hurting people?"

"Come inside Jo." Cory took his sister by the arm.

"COWARD!" she screamed and then she spat. The loogie hit the side mirror. I can see it landing to this day.

"Jo!" Cory bit out. Then he said to me: "You better get out of here Nate. Maybe see you down the road." For a fraction of a moment I considered chasing them inside and blaming temporary weakness for my actions. Begging forgiveness, letting the awkwardness subside and laughing easily about the hork on the van. Instead I turned over the engine, shifted into reverse, and took my Out.

As I eased into the general traffic, the phrase Bill Thompson had used to cheer me up earlier that same day came into my mind. It was the day he'd crashed the forklift. "Nate, bud, I know you are going to win."

I'd turned it into wasted sentiment on a surefire loser.

Two weeks after my getaway I received a reimbursement check from a Mr. Ohama for my last month's rent and damage deposit. I never saw Cory again.

And so began a snowballing effort to cover up my shortcomings with my Layne Story—a viral fog hiding my mounting guilt. Family, friends, strangers—I told anyone who would listen. Lying to so many faces, both strange and familiar, keeping nonverbal lying cues in check (looking down and to the left, putting hands to neck and face, stiffening up). Adjusting plotlines for each listener in order to avoid getting found out. Excusing inconsistencies. Blossoming the catchy, pruning the blasé. Presenting the Compassion Club as a hack organization, one unfit to control its operation. Trumping the blessedness of their cause. Dishonouring Cory. With a storyteller's wave casually downgrading his condition from HIV Positive to fullblown AIDS. Junk-feeding people on backward stereotypes of drug abuse and sexual deviance, ignoring his fight and the fight of millions suffering from the same immunodeficiency. And

Cory himself? Hammering him down to remodel as a monster. Reversing my injustices onto him. Swelling peoples' heads with force fed sketchiness...in exchange for their awe and empathy.

The tersest versions of my Layne Story were condensed lists, tiled with decadence. "Moved in with a guy, seemed normal, turned out had severe anger management problems, compulsive liar, pervert, pedophile, crackhead in a crack house, known felon, scam artist, violent, had AIDS." The imaginative, longer-winded smears were bled from these major arteries.

People react differently to gruesome gossip. The kicker was always the AIDS-reveal—my knockout punch. In that moment I knew whether or not the listener would have turned tail and run from Cory the same as I did, or stood by him. I gathered from their reactions that most would have run, and it sutured my guilt for a time. Like Allison, the French-English interpreter who was ten times more blown away by Layne's AIDS than by his pedophilia. "I'm sorry, but *AIDS*? That is disgusting." Or Tyree, the studio drummer who reduced Layne's condition to juvenile slang. "Oh man, the big A? Dude, that's worse than the HIV," he said to me, pronouncing HIV phonetically. Or Bert's severe case of the willies. Or sister Margaret's hand to her mouth.

My brother Matthew was not put out in the least. He was getting to that age. Starting to crave newness. I could see the hero worship return to his eyes every time he asked me to tell my Layne Story.

It gets cold in Sydney, Australia. You wouldn't think so, but it does.

The complete truth: I haven't done any touring. A sixth floor single with an en suite bathroom at the Sydney Habitat Hostel has been my home for eleven consecutive months. In that time, I have been outside the building twice—one walk around the block, and one outing to the zoo.

This small room, painted satin white, is spatially handicapped by a queen-sized bed and a wooden chair. The window above the chair looks out onto the dumpy adjacent building and a littered alleyway. The bathroom is a remodeled broom closet and the stand-up shower is as snug as a magician's sawing box. To get shampoo to my head, I must raise my hands close to my body. The nozzle's spray is a bit too fine, chalky even.

In the first month, the revolving hostel staff did their best to draw me into the social jet stream. Striking up conversations in the hostel canteen, plying me with invites to "killer pool" tournaments, "toss-the-boss" happy hours, and speed dating, sliding multi-coloured promotional squares in under my door if they'd missed me bringing a meal back to my room. Finally they quit trying. They started charging me the monthly rate and left me to myself. A name on the whispers of hostel staff and guests. The bent Canadian in six twelve.

My group e-mails home are as bogus as Layne—mass lying. The travel guidebooks that I bought used in Canada have notations in the margins from their previous owner. Like Layne's T-shirts, the places highlighted in them have no emotional or historical bearing on me. Every second week I take a break from my solitudes to skim a guide for a travel short, and then make it my own in the hostel computer room. Essentially I take vacations from lying to lie about my vacationing.

The reality is I haven't recovered from that gutless scene at Cory's last year, and have been in the grips of depression ever since. I started writing people with the purest of intentions, but as the lies have mounted, I have come to hate myself with a newly discovered passion.

There are good days. Days when I take a break from writing to eat lunch by the window in midday sunlight slipping between the two buildings. I meditate over the tiny blonde hairs on my hand, the gravitational pull that keeps me from floating out into the vacuum of space, the animalism of my species, or the random trivia of the world (I read in one of my guidebooks that the population of Saigon is over eight million and an average of ten people die in scooter accidents daily). Serotonin levels go high and circumstance, not I, is to blame for my indiscretions. On one of the better of these days, I loosened the noose and walked around the block. On the best, I went to the zoo.

It was ill advised. I found myself zoo bound in a record heat wave.

The UV rays blinded my indoor eyes, so I asked the taxi driver to stop at a gas station. A pair of green plastic-rimmed sunglasses had to do: I was nearly bankrupt from the compounding hostel fees. A cab ride to the harbourfront and a short ride on a ferry later, I was rolling the turnstile at Taronga Zoo.

Overdosed on the fare served in the hostel cafeteria, I ran my credit card balance nearer its limit with overpriced junk food from animal-themed kiosks. I leaned against cages with the other onlookers to watch panthers strut and penguins waddle. Watched the gorillas in their holding by the waterside with Sydney's skyline pictured in the background. Entered dark underground rooms and eyed meandering sea creatures. Learned about intertidal zones (aka foreshores)—the area of land submerged by water at high tide and exposed at low tide. The terrain can be anything from smooth mudflat to the most jagged rock shelf, and is demanding for the organisms that dwell in such neither-here-nor-there habitats.

I rode a monorail along the tall security fences enclosing the lion and tiger paddocks. One tiger leaped from its climbing apparatus to roar and swipe at a weaker cat.

The better part of my time at the Taronga Zoo, however, was spent in disgusted observation of human animals. In hindsight some of the more attentive parents and zoo security must have profiled me as a Person of Interest and kept close watch; a grown man alone at the zoo, wearing a cheap pair of dark sunglasses, burrs of tousled hair coiling unevenly from his face, neck and head, munching from a jumbo box of Camel Corn and sipping on a king-sized cup of Koala Cola—ogling, but not the attractions. But it couldn't be helped. I was transfixed. It became my opinion that the marauders dragging around me belonged in the pens. The undisciplined child in the gift shop, dried ice cream stuck to his face, whining for a toy; the meek parents giving in to the tantrum, scared that junior will stop loving them without his sixty-dollar talking grizzly bear. The North American seniors on the monorail sitting in their Depends-padded pants, the humility of which had no effect on them as they spent their remaining hours complaining about the heat, the speed of the train, the hard plastic seats, the prices, the crowds, the Australian twang and, under their wispy breaths, the Asians. The people who couldn't stop laughing when the chimpanzee squatted to take a crap in the water bucket. Damn simpletons! Then there were the mono-outfitted animal trainers in Australian bush hats, detaching from the world of humans for misconceived unconditional love from the animal kingdom: beasts that would just as soon tear an arm off as kiss a cheek for their feed. Why didn't they wake the hell up?! Then there were the actual molesters. The real-life Laynes. Out at the zoos, the public swimming pools and fast food palace playgrounds, shopping for innocence, for something to drag home and lock in their basements. Or the beastly dads who find what they are looking for right down the hall. Castrate and lock *those* up with climbing apparatus. Make *them* do tricks and lick their keepers' faces for food and empty *their* bowels to pointing and laughing. The lowlife teenagers, too lazy to give up their ferry seat to the elderly or, as I witnessed, a woman holding her pudgy infant—throw the sluggards overboard into the South Pacific aquarium. Let them strengthen those standing legs by kicking their way to shore. The cabbie visiting every reduced-lane street he could think of before dumping me off at twice the normal charge. The self-righteous backpackers in line for grub at the hostel commons, bigmouths in dreadlocks and hemp pants who think they've got backpacking, or freedom for that matter, down to a science. The dippy Canadians, maple leaves sewn onto backpacks or inked to their skin, fools who think that their country of origin automatically gives them a social head start. Why? Because a century ago the winds of emigration blew their great-grandparents to Canada? If anything, this seemed to me a glaring red and white insult to the intelligence of foreigners. The filth of humanoids in general. Their excretions alone: sneezing, coughing, farting, sweating, vomiting, pissing, shitting, bleeding. The diseases they spread that cause them to grow sickly and die. Their constant need for food, for water, for oxygen, for caffeine, for acceptance, for self-awareness, for love, for money. The misery created by their hands and the suffering ignored at their feet. And, worst of all, the secrets that amass and fester in their consciences.

Come meteor come. End it all.

I settled down to rest on my bed after cleaning the spaghetti and meat sauce I'd thrown at my white bedroom wall. I'd also cleaned up the bits of clothing I'd shredded, the mattress I'd overturned, the toiletries I'd tossed around the bathroom, the shards of glass from the bathroom mirror that I'd shattered, and the deep scores on my right hand from this breakage.

The madness of my day at the zoo gave way to clarity.

There was a time I'd thought of myself as good. I may have been babyish, an easy target, melodramatic, an absentee brother, a Sally Struthers. But I was a good person. And although my name would probably appear in the newspaper only twice in my lifetime—once going in and once going out – and, granted, I would never be anyone's dinner party anecdote *("He used to sell me paint." "That's my white bracelet he wears.")* or be anyone's go-to guy; and the lead singer of my favourite band might not like me if we were to meet someday, I was a good person. Good enough anyway.

Wrong.

NOW I sit in the pit I've dug, taking stock. In the landscape of the past twenty-five years, I see foothills of principled conduct —doors held open, money lent, strangers welcomed, garbage binned, favours granted, friendships defended...then a soaring peak of decrepitude. My defining moment the lack that has culminated in pages I write in seclusion aiming for sufficient disgust to offset my guilt. A journal I check over for spelling, grammar, and consistency, tidying my lies.

Of course, as a body of work it has now grown so wearingly large that there are discrepancies I abstain from patching simply out of writer's fatigue. For instance, the Cannabis Cup is a November tradition in Amsterdam and any Vancouverite can tell you the Molson Indy runs in August. Nor does Vancouver ever get a dry week in April, never mind an inadvertent heat wave. Most embarrassing of the asymmetries, April Fools' Day is not a national holiday, yet everyone managed that Monday off from work.

I do at least realize that even in my baser moments, I think like a writer. I realize that, on the surface, my diary of falsehoods has achieved the status of a novel. A precarious condition: your greatest accomplishment the tale of your utmost failure.

ELEVEN months have gone by. Two without seeing a physical reflection of myself. Socked in by guilt, frozen at this hardest part—where the two Laynes meet. I eat maybe once a day now. Awake, dread facing my family and friends. But mostly I cry. In between I try to sleep away the hours.

There is a trickle of depression in my family tree. When my dad recently suffered some hard years of disconnection, the doctor at the St. Thomas Psychiatric Hospital explained it to me this way: "Your father is in a cold dark train tunnel that only he has entered. Escaping the tunnel looks simple from the outside, but things look different from the inside. You can scream encouragement from the opening, but he only hears you faintly. When he feels at his worst, a train is rumbling through the tunnel—then he has to hug the tunnel walls and hold on for dear life." I also recall my mother telling the doctor that my dad's mom (who died when I was a toddler) had shown similar kinds of unhappiness. News of my demoralized late grandmother was hard to integrate. I think I still haven't found a place for it.

The Psych turned out to be nothing like the harrowing visions of medieval torture our young small town minds had ascribed to it back in the day. It was a clean, well-lit facility boasting a staff of like-minded people with a calling and a concern for their fellow man. With their help my father faced his fears and had the pluck to drag himself out of his tunnel. Me, I went to the sixth floor windowsill twice today.

ELEVEN and a half months. Two weeks before my scheduled flight home. I'm the fly trapped between screen and glass, frenzied to find the opening but unable to retrace my steps. If I could postpone return I would, but there is no more money. Yet how can I show my face? They will want to know more about my trip, to see the pictures, the stamps on my passport.

I can't come clean. If word got out, I would be a laughingstock and an embarrassment to my family. A flight to the other side of the planet, ten thousand dollars in the red, one year of life: and only a Taronga Zoo ticket stub to show for the deal. I can hear the gossip spreading.

IT'S raining today. I like it just for the change. From in here, any change out there is good. You need it.

HAD the nightmare last night. The one where I am feeding Cory to a meat grinder. My hand gets caught and I go through with him.

Cory sits in the empty wooden chair in the corner of my room. He has done this for my entire stay. During the day he's in one of his lame pot T-shirts and jeans. At night, it's his silly robe and slippers combo. He's not a ghost per say; he simply greets me with the look he gave me when I left him for good. It's not haunting or angry, but forgiving—even hopeful. What was Cory thinking? Did he expect me back? Did he know I wouldn't be able to live it down? Was I forgiven? He doesn't ever answer.

Most maddening is that I needed Cory as much as, if not more than, he needed me. His friendship, his humour, his loveliness —they were life-giving. I evoke our good times in my memory and it's like replaying a gag reel. His Random Acts of Knowledge 2001, where we had to teach one another five new things every day and which had us saying "Did you know that..." every thirty minutes, then cracking up. That hilarious day we rented a table at the Vancouver Flea Market, just because, and sold my homebrew under the table.

Cory didn't let his HIV define him. He wasn't his disease. Every day I wish I could go back.

But not all rain touches land. Some evaporates into dry thin air.

Look at me. Still writing. Pathetic.

I went to the sill again today. Came closer in my head. Imagined the silence. The broken mirror helps prevent jumping though. Hard to jump without one last look for verification.

I step around Cory to get to the sill. I feel for his hand, but he refuses to help prop me up.

STOOD upright on the sill tonight. First time. One false move...I hate myself for doing it and for not doing it. The guilt is awesome, because Cory doesn't judge.

I'M hyperventilating. I'm crying so much. I HATE myself.
Flight tomorrow.
I just can't.

MOM, Dad, I'm so sorry.

Anne, Margaret, you are the best sisters a guy could want. Matthew, don't be like me. You are strong. Be you. Things are bad for me. Must let go.

Love you forever,
Nate

MESSAGE from Louise Mills

On November 26th, 2002, Nathan let himself out of his sixth floor window at Sydney Habitat Hostel in Sydney, Australia. The driveway below killed him instantly. His death made international headlines due to his long self-confinement before giving in.

We received word on the day we were getting ready to collect him from Toronto's Pearson Airport—the place we'd last seen him alive. A police officer came to the door. My husband Ivan later replaced our doorbell. The sound of the old one had become a haunting reminder of that day. But we both still hear it in our sleep.

Nathan was sent home and we buried him next to my parents, wearing-in a pressed suit and his white rubber bracelet with the inscription TRY. Friends and family from across Canada came to pay their respects, including Dennis Zimmer, Bill Thompson, my niece Angie, and my brother Jerry.

Not a day passes that I don't wish I could fly to Sydney, go into that room, and hold my son. Have him open up to me. Tell him about our own hunches, and how much we adore his imagination. Help him again from scratch.

Over time we've gathered the strength to read Nathan's

writings through to the end. Since then, we have sought out Cory Lane in Vancouver so that Nathan's peace could finally be made. Since the day we knocked on Cory's door with Nathan's journals and a cardboard tray of extra-large coffees, we have spent more and more time with Cory and his sister Josephine. They are lovely people. Though nobody could replace the void Nathan left in our hearts, they have become honorary members of our family. I try not to think of beautiful Jo as a daughter-in-law—I might sob uncontrollably.

It was during one of our latest visits that together we decided to publish Nathan's writing. I understand that by releasing Nathan's private revelations we might raise some eyebrows. Nathan so wanted to be a good person. We see this as a way to help him reach that end. And although we cannot guarantee people will be touched by Nathan's words, all we can do is try— for his sake.

EPILOGUE

Still here.

Only on paper would I have the guts for a descent into madness and a freefall to gory romantic death.

I also tried a murder-suicide on for size. Me picking off frumpy backpackers like carnival targets—*Pop! Pop! Pop!*—then turning the automatic weapon on myself. That future didn't fit either; couldn't even get it off the rack. The vision of someone as small as me holding a badass gun was so preposterous that even my words refused to be associated with it.

I *have* been doing my share of messy crying this past year, but that's just me.

I'm on a plane bound for Toronto, making my scheduled flight, as responsible boys do. Strangely enjoying this flight. Solitude without the aloneness back in room 612. Can't say the same for the petite woman beside me who's in a struggle for her sanity.

"Bumpy flight, eh."

"Uh yah. And this Ativan was supposed to help me sleep."

She's attractive. I'd put her in her thirties and her strained tired eyes in their fifties.

"It may not seem like it, but I'm in the same boat. Hate this. I'm like one stage above wearing an adult diaper."

She let out the briefest of laughs before her nerves reigned her back in.

"If we were meant to fly we'd have frigging wings," she said in dead earnest.

"Listen, how about we do this in shifts? You sleep first. If I hear or see anything unusual, and trust me, I'm wired for it, I'll wake you and we can panic together."

"Deal. Thanks. I'm Skyler, by the way. Don't let the name fool you."

"Nate. Pleasure."

Skyler soon loosened her tight grip on the armrest and slept soundly.

Lots for me to chew over on this long flight. What can I be back in Vancouver other than a paint salesman? Should I go with my strengths as a liar and become a politician? Nah. Too much exposure. And I can't envision anyone other than Kope, Dennis, Bill and my Mom voting for me.

Hmmm.

What about journalism? Unearthing truths as opposed to burying them in lies.

Let's see here. I could shop these writings around, make this past year serve some purpose. I'd have to pump up my character's tires some, but since when did I find that hard?

There is also that other business hanging over my head. Just as Cory allowed for my lame excuses for moving out, Kope has remained loyally silent on the truth about Cory. In reality Kope was the only other person who had met him, albeit briefly (one night of six). I know for a fact Kope has caught the swirl of St. Thomas gossip that's taken up my Layne Story. He also knows there is no way Cory could be capable of the wretched deeds I pinned on him. Allowing me my lies just as Cory once granted me his pardon, I'm left to assume that in typical Kope manner he holds on to his own integrity by neither corroborating nor refuting my Layne Story. No doubt he smoothly directs the topic of conversation elsewhere. But he'd be satisfied to know where

I'm headed next. And I'll be pleased when that strain of reserve I detect in his voice when we talk on the phone dissipates.

The plane has hit a pocket of turbulence and we're bounding softly up and down. I look out of the window beside me to a still cloud, painted by twilight to a Rusty Lemon (234-36). I smile.